FIGF

THE CITADEL OF BUREAUCRACY

"What kind of weirdo book it this, anyway?" you might be asking. I'll tell you.

It's a gateway; a portal to a world like ours with one important difference: You needn't worry so much about what you say or do in this one. It's a fantasy, a cathartic adventure. In this story YOU are the protagonist. You decide what to say and where to go.

And where are you?

It's July 5, 2019. You're an Acting Policy Analyst in the Civil Service, an up-and-comer with a promising career and a fine pension at the end of it all. But it's not all smiles *und* sunshine. The government's Albatross Pay System has stopped your pay, money's tight, and six months of overtime have left you on the ragged edge.

Thank God it's Friday.

You've just got to make it through one more day before starting your vacation. Only, there's a long train ride, dodgy government campus, and slew of frustrated coworkers between you and the end of the day. Still, with diligence and a generous helping of luck, you might just see it through.

J.D. Mitchell

The Citadel
— of —
Bureaucracy

Illustrated by Matt Herring

For civil servants everywhere.

If the price of freedom is eternal vigilance,
the price of accountability is effective bureaucracy.

The Darby Complex

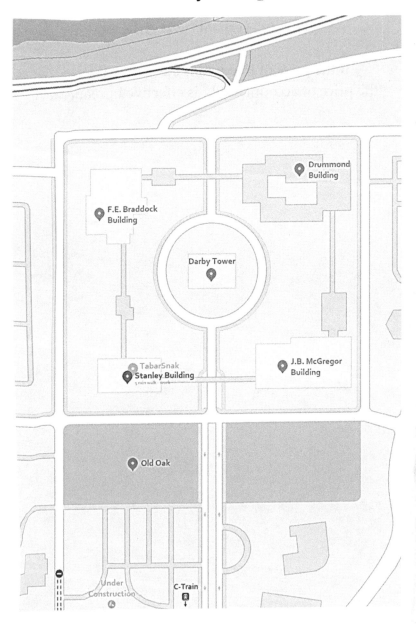

Contents

"To give real service you must add something which cannot be bought or measured with money, and that is sincerity and integrity."

   –Douglas Adams

"The best way to find yourself is to lose yourself in the service of others."

   –Mahatma Gandhi

"Politics is a strong and slow boring of hard boards."

–Max Weber

Overcoming Opponents in the Civil Service

You're an Acting Policy Analyst. What does a Policy Analyst do? Why, everything. Anything. All duties as assigned. If something needs drafting, you're ready. If a manager needs briefing, you're there. If a stakeholder needs consulting, you're on it.

Don't worry, you'll get the hang of it. Probably.

Before embarking on your bureaucratic adventure, you must first determine your strengths and weaknesses. In government terms, your Core Competencies. You're self-taught in Microsoft Office Applications and possess a wide array of policy, planning, and analytical expertise learned on the fly.

To determine how good a civil servant you are, you must use dice (the good, old-fashioned six-sided kind) to establish your Core Competency scores. If you don't own dice, just Google "roll 2d6." You can record these and other scores on a notepad or on the *Record of Adventure* form provided on page 18.

If your eyes have already glazed over, you can skip to "How to Cheat Fairly" on page 17. But if you're already struggling, I shudder to think how you'll handle the infinite policies of the Civil Service.

Core Competencies

Every civil servant has three basic Core Competencies: SKILL, STAMINA, and LUCK.

SKILL reflects your expertise and effectiveness as a Policy Analyst. Roll one die. Add 6 and enter the total in the SKILL box on your *Record of Adventure* (FRM-0001c).

STAMINA reflects your fitness and determination; the higher it is the longer you'll survive the Civil Service. Roll two dice. Add 12 and enter the total in the STAMINA box.

LUCK indicates how well you'll weather the misfortunes heaped upon you in the Civil Service. Roll one die. Add 6 and enter the total in the LUCK box.

Your SKILL, STAMINA, and LUCK scores will change a lot throughout your adventure. Keep an accurate record, including your *Initial* scores. Although you may restore Core Competency points, these totals may never exceed your *Initial* scores and may never fall below zero.

If your STAMINA ever reaches zero and you aren't given a reference, it's the last straw and you pack it in for the day. In that case, turn to **344**.

Confrontations

You will have many Confrontations in the Civil Service. The option to flee may be given, but if not, or if you get off on a good fight, resolve the contest as follows.

First, record your opponent's SKILL and STAMINA scores in an open *Encounter Box* on your FRM-0001c. The sequence is then:

1. Roll two dice and add your opponent's SKILL.

2. Roll two dice and add your current SKILL.

3. If your total is higher than your opponent's, you have struck a blow to their ego, argument or (in rare cases) body. If your opponent's total is higher, they have bested you. If both totals are the same, it's a tie—start the next *Confrontation Round* from step 1.

4. Whoever lost the round loses 2 STAMINA; reduce your or your opponent's STAMINA score.

5. Begin the next *Confrontation Round* by repeating steps 1-4. This sequence continues until you or your opponent's STAMINA score has been reduced to zero (one of you have lost the Confrontation).

6. If you lose, you'll be instructed where to turn in the relevant passage. If there's no instruction, turn to **344**.

Escaping

You might be given the option of running away from a Confrontation. If you do, lose 2 STAMINA points as you flee. Such is the price of cowardice. You may only *Escape* if specifically noted on the page.

Tests of Skill and Luck

Successfully navigating the Civil Service requires a certain measure of skill and luck. You will be called upon to *Test your Skill* or *Test your Luck* throughout your adventure, as follows:

1. Roll two dice.

2. If the total is *equal to or less than* your current respective SKILL or LUCK score, you have been *successful* or *lucky* and the result will go in your favour.

3. If the number rolled is *higher* than your current score, you are *unsuccessful* or *unlucky* and will be penalized.

4. No matter your current SKILL or LUCK, double ones are always a success and double sixes are always a failure.

Unlike Tests of Skill, each time you Test your Luck, you must subtract one point from your current LUCK score. Everyone's luck runs out sooner or later.

Restoring Skill, Stamina and Luck

Skill

Your SKILL score shouldn't change much during your adventure. A better item might increase your SKILL, but you may only use one at a time (you can't claim two bonuses for carrying two upgraded phones). Taking a Painkiller (see below) restores three (3) points of SKILL.

Stamina and Provisions

Your STAMINA score will change a lot during your adventure as you confront colleagues and undertake draining administrative tasks. You begin with a Sad Bagged Lunch but may obtain other food throughout the day. You may rest and eat only when permitted in an entry. When you do, restore four (4) points of STAMINA and strike the food from your FRM-0001c. Taking a Caffeine Pill (see below) will restore six (6) points of STAMINA.

Luck

Taking an Antidepressant (see below) will restore three (3) points of LUCK.

Remember: Your SKILL, STAMINA, and LUCK scores can never exceed their *Initial* values unless specifically instructed on a page.

Time

Time is relative, but you still have a limited well. Every delay and obstacle have the potential to put you catastrophically behind schedule. If you fall too far behind, you'll be woefully unprepared for the end of the day, but neither should you blithely rush ahead—do so and you will miss vital encounters and information. To help avoid this, you must keep track of TIME.

Your FRM-0001c has a TIME box. Write "24" inside. You'll be instructed to deduct one or more points from your TIME score as the day progresses. Each point of time represents roughly fifteen to twenty minutes.

As soon as your TIME reaches zero, you are Out of Time.

If you ever run Out of Time, turn to **92**.

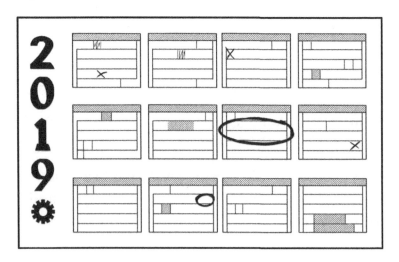

Merit

It's difficult to fail outright in the Civil Service but equally difficult to achieve anything tangible. Your performance during this adventure turns on earning MERIT. Your MERIT score starts at zero and increases by achieving measurable results. Be warned, you can also lose MERIT for underperforming or behaving in a manner unbefitting a Civil Servant.

Unlike SKILL, STAMINA, and LUCK, your MERIT score can fall below zero. If it does, it becomes a negative number, returning to zero or a positive number if you earn back enough points.

Your performance will be rated at the end of the adventure based on your final MERIT score. See **Appendix 2: Performance Review** for more information.

Equipment and Medications

You start your adventure with a bare minimum of equipment but may find other items throughout the day. You are armed with a government-issued Cellphone, ID Badge, and Laptop and are dressed business casual with a pair of sensible shoes. You have a bag (big purse, backpack, satchel, etc.) over your shoulder to hold your Sad Bagged Lunch, Folding Umbrella, and any items you come across throughout the day. You have a bit of Pocket Change, enough for a coffee and maybe a day-old muffin.

In addition, you may choose one pill to rattle around the bottom of your bag to aid you on your quest. You may only choose *one* of these three pills, so choose wisely!

A Painkiller — restores 3 SKILL points

A Caffeine Pill — restores 6 STAMINA points

An Antidepressant — restores 3 LUCK points

This pill may be taken at any time during your adventure except during a Confrontation. Once used, strike the pill from your FRM-0001c.

How to Cheat Fairly

Maybe you're a casual player and just want to find out what happens in the story. Maybe you find these sorts of books off-putting. I get it, you just want to read the jokes and enjoy the ambiance. Below are a few cheats to get you through. Just be sure your probationary period is over if you use them or you might get fired.

Story Mode

You win every test and Confrontation without even glancing at dice. You might not dominate the book in just one playthrough, but you'll get close. Close enough for government work.

A Finger in Time

When flipping to a new entry, leave a couple fingers in the last section. If you don't like the outcome (you were only curious, after all), flip back and try again.

Hints on Play

Make notes and flowchart your progress. Unlike a Civil Service critical path, this chart will be useful and enable you to rapidly progress in subsequent playthroughs. Like any government endeavour, success comes slowly if at all and rarely on the first try.

Download FRM-0001c at **www.jdmitchellwriter.com**.

Record of Adventure (FRM-0001c)

Confidential once completed

Note: Consult your H.R. Advisor before submitting this form.

Section 1: Personal Information		
☐ New ☐ Amendment ☐ Cancellation		Office Use Only

1. Name: [REDACTED]

2. Personal Identifier: [REDACTED]

Section 1.1: Merit and Time

3. MERIT	4. TIME *(At zero, turn to 92)*

Section 1.2: Core Competencies

5. SKILL	6. STAMINA *(At zero, turn to 344)*	7. LUCK
Initial:	*Initial:*	*Initial:*

Section 1.3: Possessions and Documents

8. POSSESSIONS

Cellphone	*Spare Change*
Laptop	*Pill:*
ID Badge	*Folding umbrella*

9. PROVISIONS
Sad Bagged Lunch

10. DOCUMENTS
Briefing Material

Section 2: Notes
11. NOTES

Record of Adventure (FRM-0001c)

Confidential once completed

Note: Employees must complete Harassment and Violence Prevention (WP100).

Section 3: Encounter Boxes					
1-a:		**1-b:**		**1-c:**	
Skill:	Stamina:	Skill:	Stamina:	Skill:	Stamina:

2-a:		**2-b:**		**2-c:**	
Skill:	Stamina:	Skill:	Stamina:	Skill:	Stamina:

3-a:		**3-b:**		**3-c:**	
Skill:	Stamina:	Skill:	Stamina:	Skill:	Stamina:

4-a:		**4-b:**		**4-c:**	
Skill:	Stamina:	Skill:	Stamina:	Skill:	Stamina:

19

Briefing Note

Background

You are a Policy Analyst, a small but ubiquitous cog in the cyclopean organization that is the Civil Service. Governments come and go but the Civil Service endures; you endure—have endured for six long years. You work in the Policy Implementation Directorate (P.I.D.) of the Innovation Branch (I.B.), the mandate of which is to streamline and modernize all of government. No easy feat.

The I.B. is part of the Innovation and Inter-Governmental Affairs Department (I.A.I.G.A.D.). No one pronounces I.A.I.G.A.D. the same way. You suspect a proper pronunciation might call forth an otherworldly entity from a hell plane of shifting policy tides and endless mandatory forms. It's your job to fight these very things.

Current Situation

Serving in a variety of positions, you have amassed a trove of corporate knowledge and transferable skills. This has earned you a reputation as a "doer." While ensuring your rise from entry-level Clerk to Acting Policy Analyst, your Doer Status has also made you essential to Management. That means you're on their radar. Indispensable. In demand.

Your reward has been an acting assignment, a bump in pay, and ten times your normal workload. When word got out that you could actually do things, you were writing every document, leading every working group, and making every call—essentially, doing all the things no one else had time for anymore. Only, now you're in the same boat: a boat lost in a bureaucratic sea and far from life's calm harbour.

Considerations

It's been a hard six months. Late nights, dinners interrupted by phone calls, and conversations half-heard over urgent work texts have left you isolated, drained, and demoralized. Your unit is understaffed; it has more empty boxes than an electronics store on Black Friday. Your director was seconded to another department a month ago, leaving your senior analyst to work both jobs with nary an advisor in sight. You'd leave it all behind, but no one gets total benefits, ironclad job security, and a pension anymore.

In twenty-nine years, you'll be set.

At least summer holidays are here, but that means even fewer people to do a growing pile of work. Worse, the government's Albatross Pay System left you without a paycheque *again*. You can't even afford a coffee without going into overdraft. Your finances are a teetering Jenga tower that's more air than Alder wood; one false move and…

But things are looking up. It's Friday, and you squared away your draft Government Innovation Report (the Report). You spent years on it, poured your heart and soul into recommendations supported by solid evidence and skillful analysis. Your conclusions are bold, and your solutions will cut bureaucracy and streamline needlessly complex procedures government wide.

Best of all, you finally got through to a responsive Pay Centre rep yesterday, one who was sure they could work out your issue. Just in time. You start a long overdue vacation tomorrow. By the time you get back your manager/director will have brought in TWO fresh-faced Co-op Students, the ultimate salve for a swelling governmental workload. They should have started a month ago but, well, paperwork.

Next Steps

You grab your keys and Spare Change, shoulder your bag, and head out the door. Things will turn around. You just need to get through today.

How hard could it be?

Recommendation

Turn the page.

1. The Darby Complex is a drab, concrete brutalist campus.

It's July 5, 2019, and you're pressed against the sliding doors of a CityTranspo train. Your forehead bumps the window with every lurch and jostle. Heavy rain droplets batter and stream across the glass. It's warm outside and the rain has only made it stickier, enhancing the compartment's warm baloney smell. You gaze at the rusted tracks streaking by. An inch of aluminum, plastic, and dodgy, municipally outsourced pneumatics stand between you and a gruesome death. There are no handholds, but also no need since your compartment is jammed with wet passengers staring anywhere but at one another. It's a holiday week, meaning the crowd should be thinner, but CityTranspo has cut service to maximize bottlenecks and passenger discomfort.

The C-train rounds a bend, its wheels shrieking like low-grade steel souls being dragged down the tracks to hell. The force of the turn presses your nose into the window. The train straightens aggressively, sending you into the backpack of the person behind you and the shoulder of the person to your right. None of you say a thing; the mutual support is understood.

Assuming a slightly steadier posture, you look at the impression your face left on the glass and adjust your damp bag. The corner of the laptop inside has worked its way into your hip for a third time. You wipe the fog from the window as your office hoves into view. The Darby Complex. Its main tower rises into the dark, troubled sky, its lower floors shielded behind the smoked glass breezeway connecting the buildings around it.

Known as The Citadel to its inmates, the Darby Complex is a drab, concrete brutalist campus more akin to a medieval fortification than a modern place of work. Built in 1967, the Citadel is anything but modern. Packed with asbestos, bad wiring, old pipes, and with air quality equivalent to a dank, rat-infested dungeon, the only reason the Complex hasn't been condemned is because, sure, it would leave thousands of civil servants without a place of work, but, more importantly, no government could survive the political fallout of a costly retrofit.

The train bucks and screeches as it approaches Darby Station.

Test your Luck. If you're Lucky, turn to **201**. If you're Unlucky, turn to **151**.

2

Jesus, it's already time for lunch. What a morning. You check your email, but it won't load. If you didn't already know, the network's down again, meaning you can't do much until it's back up. Might as well take your lunch break for once (hey, this is a fantasy!).

Test your Luck. If you're Lucky, turn to **316**. If you're Unlucky, turn to **48**.

3

The time has come to track down someone who can get updated stats for your Presentation and the person who sent your Report to the A.D.O. Only, do you care anymore? If not, turn to **21**. Otherwise, note down this passage and try to find one of them using **Appendix 1: Electronic Directory Services**.

If you don't know their first name or the acronym of their unit, you'll have to head to the C.P.D. to find help (turn to **156**).

4

"Ah, the healthy option! *Bon, bon,*" André says with a grin. You hand over your change and take the Muffin tucked in a waxed paper bag (add it to the Provisions box on your FRM-0001c). You pop open the milk carton and take a sip.

Roll one die. If the number is 4 or greater, turn to **287**. If it's 3 or less, turn to **165**.

5

You're in the airy, ground floor cafeteria. Most of its long, wood-veneer tables are occupied by groups of chatting civil servants. Other tables are claimed by sullen loners intent on private lunches, their phones or laptops. You smell recently defrosted lasagne and soup (both undoubtedly boiling lava hot), very slightly burnt garlic bread, and the maddening greasiness of golden fries and grilled burgers. Your stomach growls at the thought of all those precious calories.

You may eat provisions here. If you have Spare Change, you may use the vending machine first (turn to **108**). If you have two sets of Spare Change you may buy a TabarSnak (strike both sets of Spare Change if you do).

Whatever you choose, including nothing, will you sit with some colleagues (turn to **303**) or at a small table by yourself (turn to **144**)?

6

You've survived your culinary adventure with Sammi. Dropped off outside your building, the BMW or Uber you shared tears off down the boulevard, forcing Canada geese off the road. Turn to **282**.

7

"Okay, I can do it," you say.

"Good. Once the A.D. sets her mind on something she won't let it go," she replies.

"How did my Report end up in A.D.O.?"

"Let's see…C.P.D.'s Director's Office sent it up for comment. It came from their generic email account, though, so it could have been anyone."

Great. "Well, thanks anyway."

"See you this afternoon."

Lose 1 STAMINA, 1 TIME, and turn to **73**.

8

Where is it? Yes, it's jammed in the corner of your bag. You grab the Folding Umbrella, shake it loose, and open it with a satisfying "fwoomph." A sudden gust threatens to turn it inside out, but you quickly angle it into the wind, avoiding disaster. Turn to **330**.

9

You splash through the puddle that always accumulates in front of the ticket machines outside. Temporary mesh fencing keeps you from the side lot, driving you toward several large, decorative boulders on the new yet dangerously uneven concrete pads. The boulders are channeling everyone into two sluggish lines. Weaving through the crowd, you try to keep from getting stuck.

Test your Skill. If you're Successful, turn to **248**. If you're Unsuccessful, turn to **280**.

10

You try looking in E.D.S. under "Innovation Affairs" but come up with too many entries. Are they a unit, a branch, an agency, or something else entirely? And in which building? You could spend hours running around trying to find them, but you don't have that kind of time. You'll just have to try the C.P.D. Turn to **156**.

11

You talk to the Security Officer at the front desk. Luckily, he's able to verify your appointment and you sign for a Temporary Pass. It takes some time, though, and it's already been a long day. Lose 1 STAMINA.

Scanning your way through the gate, you catch an elevator to the Thirteenth Floor. Turn to **102**.

12

The trolls respond with fallacious arguments and childish name-calling, their utter lack of personal accountability undermining any reasonable discussion. Facing the maddening trio before even setting foot in your office is the last straw. Nothing is worth this; you should have started your vacation yesterday. You stalk back to the station. Your workday is at an end. Turn to **344**.

13

Halfway to your building is a lawn with a huge oak tree in the middle, its leaves whipping in the wind. With fat raindrops pelting down, will you:

Cut across the lawn to save time	Turn to **345**
Carry on down the sidewalk	Turn to **354**

14. A reedy, long-armed woman beetles toward you.

14

You turn into the elevator vestibule. A reedy, long-armed woman beetles toward you. She's wearing a suit with a knee-length pencil skirt. Her tight pumps clack a steady tattoo like a snare drum at an execution. It's Susan, and she's waving a stapled document in the air like she's signalling a rescue plane.

"Hello, Susan," you say.

She shoves the document into your hands. It looks familiar and is rife with red annotations. "I have a few notes on this analysis you did for us. I need it redrafted before I present to the A.D. on Monday."

A few? You flip through the review you conducted on her unit's policy structures, including a workflow and data analysis. You take a deep breath. She wants to alter your conclusions to fit her assumptions.

Will you:

Brush her off	Turn to **109**
Try to reason with her	Turn to **81**
Tell her you'll "get right on it"	Turn to **353**

15

"Naturellement!" André says, pouring a cup of thin-looking coffee into a brown paper cup. You hand over your change and take a Cinnabonne tucked in a waxed paper bag (add it to the Provisions box on your FRM-0001c).

You wish him a good day, fix your drink how you like it, and leave, taking a sip of scalding, tea-flavoured coffee as you go (restore 1 STAMINA).

"Bon aventure!" André says as you leave.

Lose 1 TIME and turn to **351**.

16

"Sorry, I'm out, but you can have this," you say, pulling out your lunch. A scowl flickers across his face. You're sure he's about to tell you where you can stuff the lunch, but he nods and accepts the damp brown bag. Cross the Sad Bagged Lunch off your FRM-0001c and turn to **210**.

17

The Shared Drive's slower than a...no, nothing's slower than the Shared Drive. This is going to suck, quite literally, your time. Resolve your search as a Confrontation but lose 1 TIME at the end of each *Confrontation Round*. Good luck!

MADDENING SEARCH   SKILL 9   STAMINA 4

You may end the madness (Escape) at any time by turning to **246**. If you find the file (win), turn to **142**. If you lose all heart (Stamina), turn to **344**. If you run Out of Time, turn to **92**.

18

You hit the kitchenette to clean up, trying to avoid looking at the wet food crime scene in the sink as you do.

"Network's back up!" someone cries, prompting scattered cheers from the thin Friday crowd.

You head back to your cube via the elevator vestibule. Turn to **83**.

19

"Not great, actually," you sigh.

Faye frowns and gestures for you to sit, which you do. "Sorry to hear it. Drink? I stocked up knowing I'd be stuck here all day." You nod and she pours you a cup of water, coffee, tea, or wine. She sits beside you. Having dropped her veneer of authority, Faye looks every bit as tired as you feel. "It's been a long day. What's on your mind?"

Where to start? Pay issues, understaffing, overwhelming workload, crumbling infrastructure? You touch on the issues most affecting you. It feels good saying this to the most senior person in your branch. Restore 1 SKILL and 1 STAMINA.

Faye shakes her head. "It's frustrating. I thought becoming an A.D. meant I could fix everything, but the big issues are still out of reach. Actually, that's why I called this briefing."

Turn to **211**.

20

A.D.O.? The Associate Deputy's Office tasked you with this briefing. I don't think you've been paying attention. Lose 1 MERIT.

Return to **Appendix 1: Electronic Directory Services** and try again.

21

You're well past caring about updated stats or whoever sent your Report to the A.D.O. This whole business has been one mess too many out of six months of hot garbage. You square away a few more items and clear your office for your vacation. You've done enough. Turn to **323**.

22

"Warning: BATS infesting the Tower."

"The Gov-Gov Charitable Campaign is nearly over!"

"Albatross Update: Don't expect a paycheque this week if we overpaid you."

"Tickets available for the I.B. Gov-Gov Charitable Campaign Talent Show!!!"

"GOVdocs Implementation Cancelled—You're on Your Own."

"Give to the I.A.I.G.A.D. Gov-Gov Charitable Campaign today!!!!!"

These are a few of the emails that greet you. You attack your inbox with gusto, but there's a lot to sift through.

Test your Skill. If you're Successful, turn to **95**. If you're Unsuccessful, turn to **168**.

23

The C.P.D.'s a big place. You'll need to be more specific. Return to **Appendix 1** and search again.

24

Sadie sets a drinking glass brimming with a pale, periwinkle-coloured, yoghurty concoction in front of you. It smells like a sulphurous milkshake. "What's in it?" you ask.

"You'll have to guess," she says offputtingly.

Nothing for it—you gulp it down. It's cool and smooth but chalkier and more vegetal than you expected. You're not sure you'd call it dynamic, but it ain't bad. It's sort of good after a few helpings, and somewhat invigorating. Restore 1 SKILL.

Note down your Dynamic choice and turn to **334**.

25

The E.D.S. entry for the Office of Innovation Affairs (O.I.A.) lists only its manager. You call him up. He answers and you tell him who you are.

"Oh, shoot—I have another call. Sorry," he says, hanging up.

Nuhn-uh, he's not getting off that easy. You look up his office; he's in the basement of the building next door. Time to make a house call.

You walk to the old, dirty, irregularly storied J.B. McGregor Building on the Citadel's south-east corner. One side of its concrete exterior is still rain-soaked, and its roof is a mass of metal ducts and tubing. The Department of Health (D.O.H.) must have some labs inside. You scrape open the building's crooked, steel, safety-glassed door and step inside.

Do you have an ID Badge or Temporary Pass? If so, turn to **394**. If not, turn to **233**.

26

They alternately stamp out their butts and turn off their vaporizer. Resolve your Confrontation with each CHAIN-SMOKING TROLL in turn.

	SKILL	STAMINA
VAPER	4	5
CIGARETTE-SMOKER	6	3
CIGAR-SMOKER	5	4

If you defeat all three, turn to **373**. If one beats you, turn to **12**.

27

You drop your change into the donation box (cross it off your FRM-0001c) and grab a fat Chocolate Bar. You can snarf it down now or later. If later, add it to your Provisions box. Either way, turn to **249**.

28

You scuttle to your cubicle like artillery shells are whistling out of the sky. Were you spotted?

Test your Skill. If you're Successful, turn to **84**. If you're Unsuccessful, turn to **134**.

29

You want to call the P.I.D.? Your own unit? I don't think you've been paying attention. Lose 1 MERIT.

As much as you'd like to clone yourself, science hasn't taken us to such dark vistas. Yet. Return to **Appendix 1** and search again.

30

You sneak into an elevator before the doors slam shut. A man and woman holding steaming Starbucks cups are chatting inside. She's wearing a fashionably unfashionable pair of rubber boots and a yellow rain slicker. He has on a glossy, multi-pocketed jacket with a movie star mountaineer's fit. You turn around and hit the button for the third floor.

"I can't believe Don pulled that crap," he says.

"He's such a jerk," she says.

The man scoffs. "And the D.O. told the S.M.P. *they* were the lead?"

Jesus. You have no idea who or what they're talking about, but you might have. It's unbelievable how many people gossip openly in elevators. Not you, though. At least, you don't think so...

"I was just talking to the A.D. in the Tower. Guess what happened," he says.

"She tasked you with the Treasury Audit?"

"No, a dead BAT plopped onto her desk!"

"Oh my God, I would've puked!" she splutters.

The elevator opens and you step out.

"I know! We didn't want rabies or whatever, so we moved to Room 139. She's camping there for—" The closing doors cut him off.

It's heartening in a sick sort of way that senior management is as vulnerable to Real Property decay as everyone else. Still, you'd gladly take a healthier workplace over a delicious bit of schadenfreude.

If you end up visiting the A.D. later, be sure to turn to entry 139 to avoid any unpleasant bat encounters. Make a note of this and turn to **43**.

31

The stars are aligned. The time is right. You take the sinusoidal knife and the green, eldritch stone statue from your locking cabinet. Laying the statue in front of your monitor, you raise the blood-anointed knife over your keyboard tray.

"Iä'igäd! Iä! Iä! Cthulhu fhtagn! Ph'nglui mglw'nfah Cthulhu R'lyeh wgah'nagl fhtagn!" you cry, performing profane rites ripped from your darkest nightmares, dreams sent by an intelligence so alien and absolute that it's beyond all comprehension. What's humanity next to that?

The sky goes dark with an impossible eclipse. Your building is shaken to its roots as things not meant to wake stir once more. The tides have shifted, the End of the World has come. It's for the best. You know it in your bones. It's certainly preferable to another day of senior manager briefings.

There is no other way.

Turn to **Appendix 2: Performance Review**.

32

You wing paper plates onto the lawn and pepper the avian monstrosity with cutlery. She rips and tears at the dinnerware like it had slaughtered her young. A compostable fork wedges open her beak, and she panics, thrashing back and forth.

You charge past and across the lawn. Glancing over your shoulder, you see her snap the fork in her beak like a Rancor splitting a bone. Only, she's too late. You mount the Tower's front steps in triumph and pass inside. Turn to **393**.

33

You near the end of the corridor. Barb is still at her desk. Sensing your gaze, she glances up and squints, trying to visualize her prey. You duck through a large pod of enclosed cubicles. Emerging on the other side, you hang a left and make for the relative safety of your cubicle. Turn to **376**.

34

You reveal to Sue the many, varied, and horrid things people say behind her back (while protecting your sources, of course). Sue, aghast, flees down the vestibule in tears. It was all very satisfying up to that point.

Satisfying or not, the incident isn't going to look good on your personnel file. Lose 1 MERIT and 2 TIME. You head to your cubicle. Turn to **2**.

35

You end up at the elevators. Lose 1 TIME. You decide to get some air. Turn to **72**.

36

If you're calling Basma about your Presentation, turn to **306**. If this is about an urgent request, turn to **130**.

37

You and Sammi sit at a yellow picnic table. Its paint is bubbling and flaked away, exposing the cracked wood beneath. You casually take up a taco. You've swallowed whole ghost peppers before; you've got this. Do you?

Test your Luck, adding 1 to the roll if you had four tacos. If you're Lucky, turn to **69**. If you're Unlucky, turn to **200**. If the total is *double* your current LUCK (after the deduction for this test), turn to **94**.

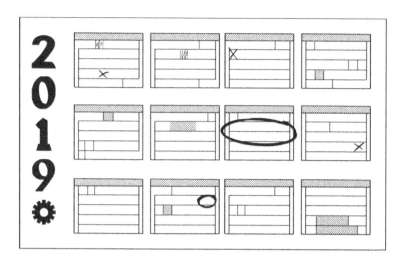

38

The Vending Machine, that oldest of foes, has won this round. It eats your change with a self-satisfied clunk.

Will you declare defeat or employ your Ultimate Gambit?

Give up and seek solace with others	Turn to **303**
Give up and sit sullenly alone	Turn to **144**
This. Ain't. Over.	Turn to **243**

39

You cancel the briefing and get a rush like a snootful of nitrous oxide. You've pulled off a day that's the icing on a six-month layer cake of chocolate misery. It's time to start your vacation. After all, *this* is what wellness looks like, not a poster or email or endless series of token meetings. Besides, they can't fire you for not making a last-minute briefing. And if they're the kind to blacklist you for that, well, greener pastures beckon.

No, you did your job and then some. Well done. You head for the station, satisfied you've done all you can for the day.

Turn to **Appendix 2: Performance Review**.

40

You rush back to your desk before getting waylaid by anyone else. Logging into your laptop, you check your inbox. It populates with a slew of emails that were caught in the system.

"Bed Bugs in Stanley Building, 4th Floor. Bug-Sniffing Dogs Deployed."

"Albatross Settlement Update: Employees lost their homes, families or lives—have a day off on us."

"We Need Your Feedback! Fill in the I.A.I.G.A.D. Integrity Survey so we can say we met your needs."

"Declare your Gov-Gov Charitable Campaign Donation today! If you do, the D.H. will sacrifice their dignity in a dunk tank to keep their at-risk pay!"

Having already given to the less fortunate, you delete the messages, try to ignore the hopefully imaginary bed bugs crawling all over your body, and turn to the task at hand.

Test your Luck. If you're Lucky, turn to **381**. If you're Unlucky, turn to **150**.

41. The pizzeria is run by Tully.

41

The Blackened Crust is run by a girthy guy named Tully. He's got an eyebrow ring, bushy goatee, tattoo sleeve, and very dodgy liver (you assume). He's the kind of guy who's obsessed with pizza ovens (tiled and wood-fired), pizza dough (double zero flour), pizza sauce (crushed tomato for brightness), pizza cheese (buffalo milk), and free cocktails for his friends.

Tully's restaurant is Urban Chic with exposed beams, dark, heavy wooden tables, dangling Edison bulbs, and mirrored, amply stocked liquor cubbies. The igloo-like, tomato red pizza oven is definitely imported from Italy. There are a few other diners in the restaurant, enjoying cocktails and margherita pizzas.

"Today's special, on the house," Tully says, sliding you each a milkshake glass with a hefty slice of white peach on the rim. Both glasses are nearly overflowing with pink and orange ice. There's a cherry in the bottom and a steel, cold-frosted straw inside.

You take a sip. The straw sticks to your lip like a tongue on a fence post in January. Your heart seizes from the super-cooled gasoline you just ingested; your brain goes into shock from the icy blow with a hint of peach administered to your frontal lobe. You're immediately drunk.

"Where do you find these guys?" you whisper-cough to Sammi.

"Easy, be an alcoholic and stay out to 2 AM. God, Tully, what do you call this thing?"

"An Alaskan Jetstream. Like it?" Tully calls over the counter. He's already working on your meals. There is no menu at The Blackened Crust.

You take another drink and press your palm into your forehead in a vain attempt hold in your brains. Your eyeballs want to suck in and pop out all at once.

Tully brings you a masterful-looking margherita pizza with fresh basil wilting on top (yes, they have vegan, gluten free options if that's your jam—Tully *knows* what you need). "You two are slowpokes. Finish those drinks so I can get your wine!"

You gawp at him in disbelief. *More* booze?

Sammi waves in your general direction. "I'm only nursing mine for their sake."

"Come on, what'll it be? Pizza's getting cold," Tully presses.

You order a high-octane Australian Chardonnay or a home-brew-worthy Chilean Cab-Sauv. Polishing off your Jetstream, you devour the pizza before he gets back. It's. So. GOOD! Tully brings your wine (twelve dollars for four ounces, thank you) and it's gone in two generous sips. Restore 4 STAMINA but lose 2 TIME.

"Round two?" Tully asks with a grin.

Sammi's game, but are you?

If you want more, turn to **218**. If you'd rather go back to the office, turn to **310**.

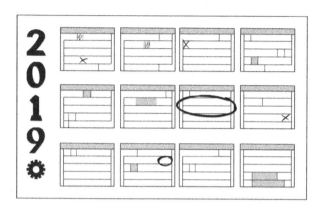

42

You take the full brunt of Barb's whinging before wrestling the name out of her.

"Joshua's in the C.P.D., not the I.A. — whatever that is. He was working on your stats. He's so useless. I don't know how the C.P.D. gets so much funding when we do all the work. That's government for you. Why do things right when you can do them wrong a dozen times." She turns back to her monitor and continues to gripe.

Lose 2 STAMINA and 2 TIME. Note that Joshua has your stats and gain 1 LUCK for the info. You slip away while you can. Turn to **208**.

43

You squeak wetly over the brown tile of the third-floor vestibule. The hall always smells distressingly of dust and burnt wires, like the noxious herald of an electrical fire. You engage in your morning perusal of office equipment, storage units, dismantled cubicle walls, and other abandoned surplus items piled against the walls, then review the familiar photo collage of a team you've never seen. After scanning signs informing you that "Wellness is Everybody's Business" and to "Think Twice" about workplace harassment, you are thoroughly motivated to start the day. Lose 1 STAMINA and turn to **125**.

44

You carry on for a good ten minutes. So does the alarm. It's very annoying, but you manage to polish your Presentation. You email everything to the A.D.O., grab your things, and bustle to the stairs. Shouldering open the fire door, you're greeted by a roiling column of hot, black smoke. This isn't thin movie smoke, it's the real deal. You fall back, coughing. The heat presses the door open, smoke broiling through like a living pillar of ash. It explodes on the ceiling, mushrooming in every direction in a choking, black wave.

You dart forward to close the door but are driven back by heat. You've never felt such ferocious intensity. The hairs on your face and arms curl. You get a searing mouthful of air filled with every toxic material an office

48

You arch your cracking back and start, sending a twinge up your spine. *Something's missing.* Physically.

If you've already lost your ID Badge, turn to **138**. If you haven't already lost it, yes, I'm afraid you have. The damn thing's always falling off, its cord breaks or plastic housing cracks, dropping out a card. You look everywhere but can't find it. Cross the ID Badge off your FRM-0001c and lose 1 TIME for the search.

How will you spend what's left of your precious lunch hour?

Get a Temporary Pass	Turn to **89**
Meet Sammi (if you saw them earlier)	Turn to **122**
Search the third floor for food	Turn to **356**
Sit in the cafeteria	Turn to **5**
Sit at your desk	Turn to **110**

49. The truck's logo is a violently yellow radiation sign.

49

You drive to the border, the county border, to a fire engine red food truck owned by Mary, a Los Angeles expat. Its logo is a violently yellow radiation sign that looks like it was pulled off an active nuclear reactor. Mary's operation does swift business. The parking lot in which she operates is packed with cars from old beaters to luxury imports. They surround The Pit—a grease-smeared patch of pavement sporting black, yellow, and red picnic tables.

You join a long line snaking its way to the food truck. Mary is triaging orders with the efficiency of a disaster response medic. The smell of roasted food is driving you mad. Mary's son lays in some fresh bins of beans and meat from which Mary furiously fills more tacos. You're up.

"What'cha want?" she hollers into the sweaty parking lot air.

Bean, beef, pork, or chicken. Flour or corn tortilla. Your favourite drink. There are no wrong choices and only two questions: How many and how hot? You can order one to four tacos that are hot, hotter, or hottest.

Jot down the number of tacos and choose a heat level:

Category 3 (Hot)	Turn to **97**
Category 4 (Hotter)	Turn to **229**
Category 5 (Hottest)	Turn to **37**

50

If you're calling Ezra about your Presentation, turn to **388**. If this is about a last-minute report, turn to **256**.

51

This day is slipping away, and your briefing is looming like a Category 5 tropical storm. You have a job you intended to do this afternoon. If you want to finalize this project, turn to **45**. If you'd rather draft or improve your Presentation for the A.D., turn to **212**. If you just want to start winding down for the day, turn to **370**.

52

Gabby bustles around the corner, unable to put off the Deputy Head any longer. Be glad, for you've avoided a fate worse than death. Lose 1 TIME and turn to **40**.

53

Fortune favours the prepared, as you well know. Reduce the briefing's SKILL and STAMINA by your Presentation's version number and resolve as a Confrontation.

BRIEFING FROM   *SKILL* 10   *STAMINA* 10
THE DECK

If you win, turn to **255**. If you lose, turn to **311**.

54

A sick dread gnaws your insides. You hunch down and run a hand through your damp hair. "You've got to help me. I'm sorry, what's your name?"

"Patricia."

"Patricia. Pat. I'm starting my vacation tomorrow. I can't handle this. Can you cancel the briefing, reschedule it—anything?"

"Look, I'm sorry, but once the A.D. gets onto something—"

"Please."

"Well, I could extend the materials deadline a bit, but that's all."

"God, yes—anything. I need all the time I can get."

"Alright, I'll send along the meeting invitation, but we need those materials before the deadline."

You assure her they'll be ready. Turn to **73**.

55

You call up Sammi but there's no answer. Either they're busy or overdid it at lunch. Either way, there's no help from this quarter. Still, restore 1 LUCK for being a clever cat. Return to **Appendix 1** and try again.

56

Napkins, seriously? You've faced this monster before and want to use napkins? I guess I can't fault you—desperate times and all. That said, your napkins flutter on the breeze and turn over in the wet grass. More out of embarrassment than any conscious decision, you charge the feral goose. Turn to **100**.

57

The timelines. God, the ridiculous timelines. They never end. For real. It's always yesterday, in twenty minutes, the day after New Year's. A Civil Servant subjected to ceaseless demands has their initiative eroded, slowly withering them into an UNMOTIVATED ZOMBIE.

These unfortunates are destined to shuffle mutely through the halls and stare blankly at their monitors until retirement. Sure, they can perform basic functions, but only when given explicit commands. But this needn't be your fate. Not if you rally. Turn to **Appendix 2: Performance Review**.

58

Your bag, weighted by your laptop, is still no match for the dreaded Canada goose. Your blows only enrage the fearless fowl, whose beak snaps one of your fingers, bloodies your right cheek, and purples your left nipple through your coat. You slip and fall. Forced to abandon your bag, you claw your way through wet grass and slimy goose droppings. The goose nips your right Achilles tendon as you escape.

Bleeding, soaked, and reeking, you limp back to the station. Your workday is at an end. Turn to **344**.

59

Sadie plonks a stemless wine glass in front of you. It's filled with a tomato-coloured preparation with black flecks and chunks of what could pass for clam meat inside. You look at her questioningly. She shrugs mysteriously.

No turning back now. You send it down the hatch. The texture is…troubling, the flavour like a seabed-grown tomato. Still, there's a certain something you can't quite wrap your tongue around. Compelling? No; but it is an experience. Restore 1 LUCK. Note down your Compelling choice and turn to **334**.

60

A fluttering goose delivers a savage bite to your rear as you flee. Lose 2 STAMINA and turn to **317**.

61

Taylor sits down with a huff and resumes their work. "You're going on my naughty list. Back to your cube, peon," they say, dismissing you with a wave.

Now you've done it. Making an enemy of the Executive Assistant, Bender of Ears, Forger of Schedules, Minder of the Keys, is a sure-fire way to fail in any office. Lose 2 MERIT, 1 LUCK, and 1 TIME.

You make a quick exit, wondering what damage you have wrought. Turn to **2**.

62

You're going to have to fight your way through this review, and it's going to suck. Resolve it as a Confrontation, losing 1 TIME at the end of each *Confrontation Round*.

GRUESOME ANALYSIS   *SKILL* 9   *STAMINA* 5

If you win, turn to **321**. If you lose, turn to **344**. If you run Out of Time, turn to **92**.

63

"Ooh, I've got a thing, sorry," they say, genuinely upset. You pine terribly. Lose 1 STAMINA and 1 TIME.

Still, maybe whatever it is will get cancelled (hey, you can hope). Turn to **312**.

64

Hmm, what time is it? If your TIME is *less than or equal to* 18, turn to **335**. If it's 19 *or greater*, turn to **77**.

65

You get to work on an Options Analysis you nearly finished six months ago. It's to streamline a frontline unit's processes, making it easier for them to serve the public. All they need is a downward delegation of authority with tighter management controls. Problems happen, but the answer isn't to tie operational decisions to senior levels. That's like asking a pilot to build their own plane, with roughly the same outcome.

You finish the paper and send it off. If they follow your advice, it'll help them serve thousands more people each year. Gain 1 MERIT but lose 2 STAMINA and 2 TIME.

Tired, you decide to take a break.

If you're in the office, turn to **247**. If you're in the cafeteria, turn to **320**.

66

You hand the Security Officer some ID and take the form. "Where do I…"

He points a nicotine-stained finger at a metal stool between a low cabinet and the door. You sit and fill out the form. It takes a long time. You hand it over and he holds out a blank temporary magnetic pass on a lanyard, pulling it away before you can take it. "Forget to turn this in and we're going to have a problem." His glare strongly implies that the problem will be your head as his ashtray.

"Got it," you reply, taking the Temporary Pass (note it on your FRM-0001c).

You head back to the cafeteria in your building; lose 2 STAMINA and 3 TIME. Turn to **5**.

67

The Vagrant stalks off in a huff. People shake their heads as they hurry from the Exclusion Zone you've created in the station. It's not your finest hour, and you feel a shameful, karmic burn. Lose 1 MERIT and 1 TIME. You press on through the side door. Turn to **361**.

68. A roiling column of smoke stains the clearing sky.

68

You join a small crowd at the Evacuation Point in front of your building. Everyone shrugs and chuckles at the latest false alarm. The fire trucks arrive. You feel bad that they have to go through the paces of another false alarm.

Only it isn't.

The casual scene shifts to one of intense action. A firefighter urges everyone back. Thick, black smoke broils against the cafeteria windows, pressing against the glass like a bilious demon hunting for any opening, any crack through which to escape.

You go cold. Minutes earlier, you had entertained the idea of ignoring the alarm. For what? To refine a last-minute briefing? The notion shrinks like burning paper in the face of the fire's murderous reality.

A third-floor window blows out. Red-orange flames lick the side of the building, and a roiling column of smoke stains the clearing sky. Normally limp fire hoses engorge and spew water into the breach. Aghast, you stand witness to the elemental battle. That's when you realize it's time for your briefing.

Do you even care anymore?

If you're determined to see it through, turn to **313**. If you'd rather inform the A.D.O. of the fire and go home to hug your dog or cat or fish, or whomever, turn to **39**.

You break out in a sweat and your nose runs faster than an Olympic sprinter, but you maintain. The tacos are delicious. Simple yet wonderful. You understand why people come from all over for this. Restore 2 STAMINA for each taco you ate. If you ate the hottest sauce, also restore 1 LUCK for having survived, for Mary is an AR-DENT COOK, whose fiery and flavoursome fare has overwhelmed more than one diner. Your tolerance is irrelevant, Mary knows it and will push you to vistas of heat and flavour beyond your wildest imaginings.

Comfortably full, you and Sammi return to the BMW. Lose 3 points of TIME and turn to **6**.

70

Gripping the galvanized fence, you put one leg between the misaligned sections. With a bit of prying and pushing, you wedge yourself through and stumble onto the other side. Picking your way through rubble, you're forced to hop through a puddle between a gravel pile and the wide, watery hole. Only, the puddle is much deeper than it appears. You plunge into a flooded pothole up to your calf. The gasoline-slicked surface splashes up your leg. You lose your balance on the rough bottom and windmill desperately, fighting for balance.

Test your Skill. If you're Successful, turn to **349**. If you're Unsuccessful, turn to **314**.

71

These are OfficePlace 2.5 cubicles with walls so low they might as well not exist. Like a ponderous carnivore, Barb catches movement out of the corner of her eye. She rears about and lumbers to your hiding place, peering under the desk to see what sort of maniac is huddling beneath. You crawl out, red-faced, and grimace at the odious fish Barb had the temerity to microwave. Turn to **399**.

72

You walk out of the building and into the freshening air. It isn't sunny but neither is it raining, and the cloud cover isn't quite as oppressive as it was this morning. Dodging the worst of the standing water in the forecourt, you head to the boulevard ringing the campus like a moat.

Where will you walk?

Westward to the 'burbs	Turn to **380**
North along the river	Turn to **78**

73

If you're working in your office, turn to **273**. If you're working in the cafeteria, turn to **350**.

74

Thanks to Barb (you never thought you'd say that), you know who to contact for your stats. You call up Joshua in the C.P.D. He's not in Stats, so it's strange they would task him for help, but you've heard good things. He picks up.

"Hey Josh, I'm calling from P.I.D. My boss said you were working on some stats for my Report. I don't suppose you have those handy?"

"Oh, hi. Yeah, I've got some data together. It's kind of draft, though," he says.

"Anything's good. Hey, you don't work for Stats—who sent you the tasking for my Report?"

"Some manager they've reassigned—the Office of Innovation Affairs (O.I.A.) out of my directorate. You'd better talk to him if you want to know more. I'll email you those stats."

You thank Josh and hang up. An innovation office in the C.P.D.? That seems like a horrible duplication—your whole branch is dedicated to government innovation. The C.P.D. is only supposed to provide horizontal policy support. Strange. Still, maybe there's a valid reason. You'll have to talk to the O.I.A. manager to find out.

The stats arrive and you review them. They seem to confirm what a hundred Red Tape Initiatives would never solve: there are too many cogs between decision-makers and frontline civil servants. There are so many administrative fingers in operational pies that there's more flesh than dessert. The number of senior manager information requests and time tracking data speak volumes. They're preliminary and limited to a few departments but striking. You update your Presentation with this information. Increase its version number by 2 but lose 1 STAMINA and 2 TIME.

If you're interested in talking to the O.I.A. Manager, you look them up in the E.D.S. (turn to **25**). If you'd rather not, turn to **323** instead.

75

Barb counters your feeble attempts to disengage with whinging aplomb.

Resolve your Confrontation.

SHIFTLESS MOANER   *SKILL* 8   *STAMINA* 8

If you win, turn to **235**. If you lose, turn to **344**.

76

Have you already tried calling the Pay Centre? If so, turn to **358**. If not, go get paid by turning to **64**.

77

You bring up the Pay Centre Rep's email. They naively put their phone number in their signature block. You'd bet your pension that number will be gone in two weeks. There's no resource more sought-after than a diligent Pay Centre Rep.

You dial them up. The phone rings and rings and rings. You're resigning yourself to leaving a message when a bright, chipper voice comes on the line. "Hi, this is Drew. How can I help?"

"Hi Drew, I spoke with you yesterday. You said you thought you could work out my pay issue?" You give them your name and Personal Identifier, praying to the Janus-faced God of Finance and H.R. to grace you with favour.

"Yes, I'm glad you called. I think I know the issue. Hold on while I bring up your file."

You grin. It's too good to be true.

Test your Luck. If you're Lucky, turn to **387**. If you're Unlucky, turn to **207**.

78

You walk through parking lots, across the Parkway, and along the water's edge. Birds are chirping and Canada geese doze on the cropped, dropping-littered lawns. The breeze is stronger by the water, keeping you cool. You follow paths along the river, down slopes and up rises, under the trees, and past picnic areas. It would be perfect but for the near-constant *ding-ding*, "On your left!" from spandex-clad, speed bike-riding maniacs; they race down the path like they're in the Tour de France.

Still, you manage to enjoy your stroll. Restore 1 STAMINA and 1 LUCK for increased peace of mind but lose 2 points of TIME. Turn to **205**.

79

"You're on!" they say. Your heart leaps. This day is looking up!

Restore 1 STAMINA for the boost but lose 1 TIME. Turn to **312**.

80

Taylor looks at you askance, jaw set. If they were wearing earrings, they'd be coming out. "Oh, hell no."

You've stoked the ire of a BRUTAL ASSISTANT. God help you, for no one else will. Resolve your Confrontation.

BRUTAL ASSISTANT   *SKILL* 9   *STAMINA* 8

If you win, well, there's no winning here, turn to **61**. If you lose, turn to **344**.

81

"I had Central Stats triple-check the data. Your own team validated the numbers. They're solid," you say.

Sue scowls. "No, no, I need the numbers to support what I *know*."

"That's not how data works, Sue."

"I'm the subject matter expert, the analysis should match my opinion."

Your response?

Tell her to take it up with your boss	Turn to **90**
Tell her it's her problem	Turn to **228**
Give *her* some notes—personal ones	Turn to **363**

You wrestle the name out of Barb relatively quickly. "Joshua in the C.P.D. is working on the stats for your Report. He's so useless. I don't know how the C.P.D. gets so much funding when we do all the work. That's government for you. Why do things right when you can do them wrong a dozen times." She limps on, griping all the way. Lose 1 STAMINA and 1 TIME.

Note that Joshua has your stats and gain 1 LUCK for the info. You head in the other direction while Barb whinges on. Turn to **154**.

83. *"We're late for the meeting!"*

83

Gabby from the Industry Unit rushes toward you, shawl billowing. She's flustered bordering on raving. You take her by the arm. "Is there a fire?"

She seizes your bicep and pulls you along. "We're late for the meeting!"

You don't have a meeting now. "What meeting?"

"The Red Tape Initiative! The Deputy Head is already here!"

A dreadful shudder runs through you. "No!" you cry, pulling away; but fear has given Gabby uncanny strength. She holds you in place.

What do you do?

Give in — Turn to **384**

Reason with her — Turn to **360**

Shove her into a waiting elevator — Turn to **131**

Tear yourself away — Turn to **264**

84

Seconds pass. Nothing. Good, they didn't see you. If you're lucky, they'll stop by your boss's cube and just get on with their meeting, leaving you in peace. They can work with him next week; you've got to attend to other things. Turn to **366**.

85

The Vagrant sees you. He sends Rufus after the geese, the dog springing away like a surface to goose missile. The birds fall away in a waddling arc. You throw the Vagrant a wave of thanks. He nods in return. Liberated from their captors, the other civil servants bolt from the Tower while they can. Your business, however, lies inside. You dash forward.

If you encountered a Mother Goose before reaching your building this morning, turn to **143**. If not, turn to **393**.

86

Barb limps by without seeing you. You beat a hasty retreat to your unit. Turn to **154**.

87

Nope, not today, you're not going to risk it. You've done all you can. You send the A.D.O. your Presentation, pack up, and head outside. Turn to **68**.

88

You've got Dominic's number. "Your unit wants an answer from mine today, in writing?" He sits back with a smarmy smile. You ask Basma for a sheet from her notebook, which she tears off and hands to you. You take out a pen and set to writing.

"Please contact my supervisor at the following email address or phone number…"

You stand, hand over your unit's official reply, and sweep out of the room with Basma in tow. Lose 2 TIME and turn to **367**.

89

The main Security Office is in the F.E. Braddock Building on the Citadel's north-west side. You take the elevated breezeway. The air is dusty and close, and the smoked glass and concrete make for a gloomy stroll, though the red teardrop pendant lights have a certain charm. On your right, the Tower rises into the clearing sky. The A.D.'s in there. Waiting.

You make it across and head to the ground floor. The Braddock Building's front lobby is a veritable jungle of plastic plants, cedar wall panels, and grey marble. Approaching the security kiosk, you tell a grimly silent Officer that you need a Temporary Pass. After eyeballing you for a sufficiently unfriendly period, he gestures mutely across the lobby.

You cross to a plexiglass security barrier and turn. "I just—?" The kiosk officer leans over. *Ka-chunk!* The barrier parts.

You hurry through and up a tiled staircase to a door marked "Security." Turn to **234**.

90

Sue huffs and puffs. "Your supervisor tasked you with this. Your unit provides a service. I *demand* you bring your analysis in line. It's my report, it should reflect what I know!" Lose 1 STAMINA.

Oh, she *demands*, does she? That's it, you've had enough. Turn to **363**.

91

The food's really good. It isn't anywhere near beef, bacon, or cheese, nor Transcendent, Bodacious, or Mystical, but it's filling and delicious. You wolf it down. Maybe that cleanse did clear your palate after all. Restore 4 STAMINA.

Sadie sidles up to your table. "I've got something *really* special for you two."

"I'm game," Sammi says, looking to you.

How's your game?

If it's on, turn to **357**. If it's over, turn to **46**.

92

Look at the time! This day really got away from you. If you're away from the office, you rush back. Turn to **395**.

93

He leans back and holds up his hands. "No can do. I'm swamped. Just feed A.D.O. a line and blow it off. They can't fire you." Lose 1 STAMINA.

"That's a terrible attitude," you say.

Click. "Hey, it's all pensionable." Lose 1 STAMINA.

You take a lap of his office. "I think I know why you're in the basement."

Click. Click, click. "Take my advice—keep your head down and don't make waves." Lose 1 STAMINA.

If you haven't had an aneurism, turn to **343**.

94

You can't seem to stop eating the excruciatingly delicious tacos. They're an inferno inside you, but each burn is a pleasure, each sting a joy. You can't feel your tongue, lips, or face. Sauce is everywhere; it's coursing through your veins. But you're fine. No problem.

You stumble back to Sammi's car and start back to the office. You'll make it in no—*guuuurgle.*

Was that your stomach?

Baruughl-squeeee. No, it's lower. And too late.

You've fallen afoul of an ARDENT COOK, whose fiery and flavoursome fare has spelled disaster for the most stalwart diners. Your tolerance is irrelevant, Mary knows it and will push you to vistas beyond imagination. While you have a long, unpleasant afternoon in store, your workday is at an end. Turn to **344**.

95

You blast through your inbox like a cocaine-fuelled investment banker through other people's money, answering priority messages, deleting useless forwards, and declining meetings that are a waste of time (i.e., most of them). You set your out of office auto reply for 4:00 PM. Might as well be optimistic. You're forced to dig around the Shared Drive to deal with a few taskings, but you've got everything tracked and filed. If only every morning were this smooth. Lose 1 STAMINA and 1 TIME then turn to **76**.

96

You tell him you've looked everywhere but can't find your badge. He sighs heavily, yanks open a drawer like he owes it seventeen years of support payments, and slaps a form onto the desk. "Fill that out and give me photo ID." Turn to **66**.

97

You and Sammi sit at a black picnic table with chipped and scratched paint. You have your drink ready, having been warned about the delicious heat in store. You're worried, but certain you can take their mildest sauce. Can you?

Test your Skill, adding 1 to the result if you ordered four tacos. If you're Successful, turn to **69**. If you're Unsuccessful, turn to **200**. If you roll double sixes, turn to **94**.

98

Where is it? Yes, it's jammed in the corner of your bag. You grab the Folding Umbrella, shake it loose, and open it with a satisfying "fwoomph." A sudden gust threatens to turn it inside out, but you quickly angle it into the wind, avoiding disaster. Turn to **9**.

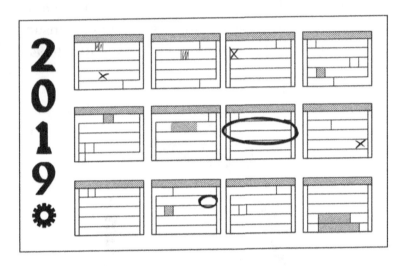

99

Heart pounding, you mention that you're free for lunch (you'll make it your business to be free, briefing or no briefing), and that, if they cover the cheque, you could find it in your heart to lend them your badge.

Will they or won't they?

Test your Luck. If you're Lucky, turn to **79**. If you're Unlucky, turn to **63**.

100

You deke right, then left — no, you slip and go down! The COBRA-CHICKEN sacks you like a 200-pound defencegoose. Only this opposition plays dirty. She lays into you with brutal precision, bruising your eye, cracking your cheek, and breaking your nose with her savage beak. You try to smother her with your jacket, but she gets away. Struggling to your feet, you spit out a tooth. That. Is. It.

The battle that follows goes down in Citadel and YouTube history but leaves you unable to walk unassisted, let alone deliver a briefing. Your workday is at an end. Turn to **344**.

101

You remember to hold back the drawer's reckless sally, sparing your kneecap another sound bashing. Turn to **213**.

102. A creature shoots out of the hole like a bat out of hell.

102

You step out of the elevator and take a steadying breath. You've never briefed an A.D. before. Directors, sure, but this is totally different. A.D.'s have the authority to actually do things.

You wander down the hall. As annoying as this day has been, and as unprepared as you feel, this really is an opportunity.

Only, the A.D.'s assistant isn't at her desk.

Where could they be? You're expected. Frowning, you knock and open the door. The lights are off, the desk clear. The washroom door is closed; maybe she's in there. You roam inside and hover near the desk. There are awards everywhere. Photos and mementos adorn the desk and wall. It's tidy but there's some dusty grit on the desk. You lean in.

What the hell was that?

You heard a chittering from somewhere.

You scan every corner, every shadow for God-knows-what then gaze up slowly. A cavernous hole in the drop ceiling looms like a black, pitiless eye. A creature shoots out, flapping and fluttering like a bat out of hell. Which it is.

You grab the keyboard off the desk, its cord slashing the air as you fend off the flying rodent.

Resolve your Confrontation.

RABID BAT   *SKILL* 4   *STAMINA* 4

If the Bat lands a single blow, turn to **355**. If you manage to kill or drive it off (dealer's choice), turn to **251**.

103

You've made it to the end of the day. Well done! All you need now are updated stats for your Presentation and to track down the prick—*ahem*—the *person* who sent your report to the A.D.O. Turn to **370**.

104

You approach the trio and smile. "Hi, would you mind moving behind the yellow smoking line? I know it's a bother with the rain and all, but your smoke gets in the doorway."

They scowl at one another then at you. Your appeal to their better natures has failed, for the trolls have none. Turn to **26**.

105

You follow Adam past the elevators and washrooms to the Shared Equipment Area. There's nothing in the printer/copier's output tray. The touch screen console is dark. He mashes it with his fingers, but nothing happens.

What will you do?

Press the console power switch   Turn to **216**
Hunt for the main power switch   Turn to **237**
Check the power cord   Turn to **186**

106

You show Bryce your boss's n— Wait a minute, you can't have picked up your boss's note on this playthrough! You clever devil. Unfortunately for you, Bryce knows very little, being so new and on a different team. That said, you have no note to show him. Return to **126** to learn your fate.

107

The C.G.U. Supervisor perks up and waves to you. "You're here! Can you update us on P.I.D.'s deliverables?"

You take a tentative step away. "My boss isn't here today, and I've got this new tasking..."

"You can take some notes for him. We'll just be a few minutes. I wouldn't ask but it's important." Their smile offers no assurance.

"Alright..." you say, grabbing a notepad from your cubicle. They fill you in, and then some. Then it's your turn. You tell them what you know about your unit's various files. They all have questions and endlessly discuss how P.I.D.'s files align with the new versions of existing branch priority streams. It's torture, but you take notes as best you can. Meeting adjourned, you slink back to your cube. Lose 2 STAMINA and 2 TIME. Turn to **366**.

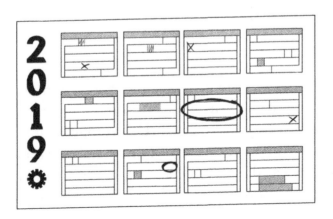

108

You strut up to the brick of a vending machine. Its black metal housing is dented, its glass greased by the fingers of drained office drones desperate for the high-octane snacks inside. Nose to the glass, you rub the Spare Change between your fingers, a gunslinger ready for the draw. You and the Machine have faced off many times; sometimes you win, sometimes you lose, but you're wise to its tricks. You glance over your shoulder, jam change into its slot, and make your play.

Roll one die and add your SKILL score. If the total is *less than* 10, turn to **38**. If the total is *between* 11 and 13, turn to **120**. If the total is *greater than* 13, turn to **137**.

109

"Sorry, Sue, this is too last minute," you say, skirting her.

You're met by a staccato clack of heels and her out-stretched hand. "No, no, I just didn't have time to go through it until this morning."

Yeah, because you've been trying to do everyone else's job all week, you don't say. Lose 1 STAMINA.

Will you next try:

Reason	Turn to **81**
Lies	Turn to **353**
Cold, Hard Truth	Turn to **363**

110

You reach your tiny cubicle in the third floor's back corner and wedge yourself behind the desk. If you have any Provisions, you may eat a meal now. The network's still down so you bring out your phone. After doing a bit of doom scrolling—things aren't looking good for the sitting government, country, or world at large—you catch up on social media and watch a few silly cat videos. It's good to disconnect, figuratively, for a bit. Restore 1 STAMINA but lose 2 TIME.

If you're still hungry and would like to search the floor for food, turn to **356**. Otherwise, turn to **302**.

111

Screw. This. These timelines are totally unacceptable. You fire back a response requesting an extension, citing a lack of resources and a conflicting request from the A.D. By the time they get back to you, you'll already be out of the office. It won't reflect terribly well on you, but who cares? Why the hell *didn't* they consult the P.I.D. to begin with? Honestly.

Lose 2 STAMINA and turn to **3**.

112

There's nothing for it. You throw your raincoat over your head and sprint like a marine taking a hill. You run a literal gauntlet of powerful, snapping jaws; your world becomes a confusion of hisses and honks, buffeting wings, and bone-mashing hammer blows to your back, arms, and legs.

Roll two dice and deduct the total from your STAMINA. If you survive the assault, turn to **285**. If not, I'm afraid you aren't going to make your briefing. In fact, you'll be lucky to make it to the hospital alive. Turn to **344**.

113

What will you deploy against this hell-spawn?

Napkins   Turn to **56**
A Vegan Cupcake   Turn to **241**
Compostable Plates and Cutlery   Turn to **32**
Forget it and try to get around her Turn to **220**

114

If you ran into Sammi on your way to the office, turn to **238**. If not, turn to **290**.

115

The combination of food you ate tears through your insides with extreme prejudice. You totter to the washroom before finishing your meal. The commode is as white and aspirational as the rest of the place, though it's hard to focus on walls urging you to be a "Wellness Warrior" and "Your Best Self" with more immediate urges radiating through your guts.

Unfortunately for you, Sadie, a slave to trends, presently follows the Medieval Diet. It calls for breads enriched with plaster, sauces cut with brine, and ash—nature's best cleanser—in everything. Vegan food is good, but not when it's prepared by a VEGAN SADIST, whose quest to elevate subsistence foods knows no bounds. Unlike your colon. Turn to **344**.

116

You storm through the steam tunnels, muttering to yourself. Gain 1 MERIT for uncovering what happened to your Report and for connecting with a rival—I mean, partner—unit. Now that you know of its existence, you can factor it into (that is, out of) your workflow. You head back to the office; lose 3 TIME.

If you're not Out of Time and know who has your stats (and you still need them), note down this passage and look them up in **Appendix 1: Electronic Directory Services**. If you don't know who has them or really don't care, turn to **323**.

117

Man, this presentation sucks. You just can't make it click. If only you had more time. You rest your head in your hands and despair. It's going to need more work and a second pair of eyes. You also need updated statistics from the C.P.D., but that'll have to wait until after (if) the network's back up. Lose 3 STAMINA and 3 TIME.

If you have a copy of your Report, note Presentation v.2 in the Documents box of your FRM-0001c. If you don't, record v.1 instead. You save the Presentation to your Desktop and decide to take a quick break.

If you're in your office, turn to **247**. If you're in the cafeteria, turn to **320**.

118

Lose 1 TIME. Will you go back to your cubicle the way you came (turn to **33**), or cut through the elevator vestibule (turn to **14**)?

119

"I don't care for coffee," she says, as if you'd offered her bacterial sludge from a septic tank. You know quite well that she drinks coffee. Lose 1 STAMINA and turn to **194**.

120

A piece of candy falls and a second trembles in the Machine's steely grip.

If you wish, you may *Test your Luck*. If you do and are Lucky, turn to **137**. If you're Unlucky, turn to **243**. If you'd rather not tempt fate, turn to **149**.

121

"B*on*, excellent choice," André says.

You hand over your change and take a Bag of Chips. Add it to the Provisions box on your FRM-0001c. You wish him a good day and take a long, refreshing gulp of soda as you leave. Restore 1 STAMINA.

"*Bon aventure!*" he calls after you.

Lose 1 TIME and turn to **351**.

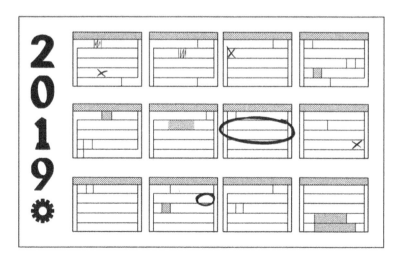

Sammi answers. "Just headed out. Meet me out front."
Excellent. You join a light flood of bureaucratic refugees
fleeing the building. Like you, many will rush to bars
and restaurants eager to relieve them of their pay in an
hour or less.

Sammi pulls up in a sleek, black BMW. Like all BMW
drivers, Sammi drives with an aggressive disregard for
the wellbeing of others. You hop in, your need to self-
medicate outweighing any sense of self-preservation.

"Where to?" they ask.

You give them a glare. "We need to be quick this time."

"Trust me!" Sammi toots the horn for emphasis.

Where *do* you want to eat?

The Blackened Crust (Pizzeria)	Turn to **41**
Los Alamos Tacos	Turn to **49**
Sadie's Vegan Charcuterie	Turn to **179**

123

You push past the unkempt Vagrant and make for the side door, chased by the crowd's judging stares. Remember to deduct 2 STAMINA for your flight and turn to **361**.

124

You hear a raised voice from a nearby meeting room.

Will you:

Investigate	Turn to **365**
Hurry along	Turn to **169**

125

You trudge over thin, grey carpet, quickly threading a labyrinth of cubicles; the maze of sound-dampening fabric does little to dull the frustrated howls of the civil servants within.

Do you want to stop by your boss's cubicle (turn to **259**), or head to your own and get to work (turn to **378**)?

126. Bryce is so mesmerizing

126

You jog nimbly upstairs. The pocked walls are cream-coloured; the landings smell of gritty dust and vinyl anti-slip strips. You make the third floor just as the crash door pulls open. Bryce steps into the stairwell. He's new. A friend of yours, desperate for help, hired Bryce from another department sight unseen.

Not wanting to be rude, you introduce yourself. Bryce is tall, lanky, and engaging. His eyes sparkle, and he has an inviting smile. You get to talking about your mutual experiences. He's great. After running through work, you turn to where you were born and how you were raised. You have SO much in common.

The minutes fly by. You don't notice the way the strap of your bag has started to chafe your shoulder, or how you've begun to shift your weight between increasingly sore feet. He tells you about all the fabulous places he's travelled and wants to hear about where you've been. People squeeze by to go downstairs then back up to the office. Bryce is so *mesmerizing*.

It's too late. You've fallen prey to a dreaded TIME VAMPYRE. You'll certainly not have enough time to finish your tasks today. Honestly, under Bryce's thrall, you might not even care. Turn to **344**.

127

Okay, you need a copy of your Report to start this presentation. You bring up the Shared Drive Explorer window. It's empty. Your Outlook inbox fades, the cursor becoming a swirling blue icon of perpetual consternation. "Network's down!" someone shouts from nearby. *No. Not now.* You shake your laptop in vain. Wait, there's still a chance!

Test your Skill. If you're Successful, turn to **318**. If you're Unsuccessful, turn to **244**.

128

The work is a slog, the processes interminable and prone to failure, yet there's never enough time. Those ground up in the Civil Service's relentless gears have all joy crushed from their soul until they devolve into a TWISTED WIGHT. These wretches are relegated to special projects where they talk only of doom and failure, doing nothing to avert it and celebrating its inevitable arrival. But this needn't be your fate. Not if you carry on. Turn to **Appendix 2: Performance Review**.

129

You stop by Ezra's cubicle. "Wow, you wear that suit better than me," they say. "Oh, the boss didn't give me any extra work for today. If you need help this afternoon, just give me a call."

A suit *and* volunteering to help? You'll make sure this is reflected in their Performance Agreement. Note down that Ezra can help you this afternoon. Lose 1 TIME and turn to **302**.

130

You forward the tasking to Basma. She responds immediately and is happy to help. However, she's just a co-op student—a really good one—but this work requires someone with more knowledge and skill. She'll do it if you ask but will struggle into the evening after getting a short extension. The work won't be to the unit's usual standard, and it'll be a stressful and demoralizing experience for Basma. If you still want her to do it, lose 1 LUCK and turn to **3**. If you want to try something else, return to **254**.

131

You shove Gabby into the elevator, but not without injury. Lose 1 STAMINA. "It's for your own good," you say, hitting "B" before she can recover. The doors shut with a jerky clunk as Gabby hurls herself into the other side. You breathe a sigh of relief and set off to your office, confident you've saved two lives. Turn to **40**.

132

You give Barb an unimpressed nod and turn to leave.

"I bet you have a great lunch. I'm stuck with tuna casserole. Again," she says.

Will you:

Say your lunch isn't so great	Turn to **187**
Try something else	Turn to **253**

133

The phone rings and rings. You're resigning yourself to leaving a message when a bright, chipper voice comes on the line.

"Hi, this is Drew. How can I help?"

"Hi Drew, I spoke with you yesterday. You thought you could work out my pay issue?" You give him your name and Personal Identifier.

"Yes, I looked into things. I think I know the issue, hold on." You grin. It's too good to be true. A bit of warmth drains from Drew's voice. "Yeah, I thought so—the H.R. side isn't jiving with the pay side."

You rest your head in your hand. It was a mistake to take this acting assignment. All it earned you is a stop in pay and a raise in workload. You'll never make that mistake again.

"I've started the paperwork for emergency pay. You should get it in two days," he says.

It'll mean the same problem in two weeks and tax problems down the road, but at least you can eat and pay rent. You thank him for doing what he could. Lose 1 TIME and 1 LUCK.

Note down that you got paid and turn to **51**.

134

The C.G.U. manager calls your name. You grit your teeth and stand back up. Turn to **107**.

135

You want to use napkins against these monsters? I guess I can't fault you, desperate times and all. That said, your napkins just flutter on the breeze and turn over in the wet grass. More out of embarrassment than any conscious decision, you charge ahead. Turn to **112**.

136

The Vagrant has an incisive counter to each of your arguments. Who is this guy? He presses his advantage, sending you back with a dirty finger to your chest. "You think you can make a difference? I *am* you. Thirteen years in that fuckin' prison," he says, gesturing wildly at the Citadel. "What'd it earn me?" He holds up his dirt-streaked wrists. "Break those golden handcuffs before they break you."

You fall back in apoplectic shock. He's right. What is the point? Why did you even come in today? For another pointless chore? To polish a policy that no one will read? You should've taken your vacation weeks ago. Defeated, you make for the platform. Stress Leave beckons.

Turn to **Appendix 2: Performance Review**.

137

You shake the Machine left and right, front and back, until TWO snacks drop out. You've proven your supremacy against the Machine. Clutching your trophies, you strut triumphantly through the cafeteria.

You may eat one or both now (such is your right) or note one or both as Provisions on your FRM-0001c.

Now, will you sit:

With some colleagues	Turn to **303**
By your lonesome	Turn to **144**

138

Cross one item off your FRM-0001c that isn't a Document, your Cellphone, or Laptop. If you have nothing left to lose, you're wrong: lose 2 STAMINA for straining your back. Turn to **386**.

139. The A.D. regards you from her chair.

139

You head to Boardroom 139. The A.D.'s assistant lets you in. It's much bigger than anything in your building; it has a long table surrounded by blue office chairs and more chairs around the walls. There's a projector, big TV, flipchart, and sideboard set with drinks and half-sandwiches. The A.D. regards you from her chair, stands, and sweeps toward you. She's barefoot with a jacket draped over her shoulders and is wearing a green skirt, sleeveless blouse, pearls, and leaf earrings.

"Hi, I don't think we've met," she says with a warm smile. "I'm Faye. How are you?"

What will it be?

The truth   Turn to **19**

Pleasant deflection   Turn to **294**

140

"It was terrible. The train was late, I got soaked on the way in, and the network went down. You'd think the government could keep one lousy network going, but no," she gripes. Lose 1 STAMINA and turn to **253**.

141

You open PowerPoint and get to work.

Test your Skill. If you're Successful, turn to **196**. If you're Unsuccessful, turn to **47**.

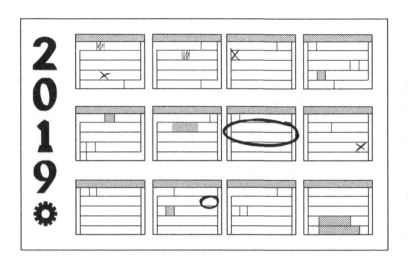

142

Holy crap, you found it! You send Grant the file. He responds immediately. "O.M.G., thank you so much! You're a lifesaver!"

You are, too, metaphorically. This is related to a major I.B. initiative, and your assistance helps Grant bring it to fruition. Gain 1 MERIT and turn to **114**.

143

Fearless and intractable, a single goose holds the field, driving off Rufus with merciless snaps and "hyønks." You glare at the bird. It's her, you're certain of it. The way she's limping and look of recognition in her black, beady eyes—it's that godawful Mother Goose from this morning, and she's between you and your goal.

What will you do?

Charge—she's going down!	Turn to **100**
Look for something to use	Turn to **113**
She's just one goose: go around	Turn to **220**

You sit at a table by the windows and stare out at the parking lot. The sun is struggling to break through the clouds like an external candidate through a government hiring process. You drum your fingers on the particleboard veneer and let your mind wander.

That's enough of that.

The network is still down, so you bring out your phone. After doing a bit of doom scrolling—things aren't looking good for the sitting government, the country, or the world at large—you catch up on your social media. It's great to disconnect from work for a bit.

Restore 1 STAMINA despite the state of the world but lose 2 TIME. Turn to **257**.

145

You've got I.T. in your contacts and give them a ring. After dialing through the menu, the line rings twice and drops you into a hold message.

"Thank you for calling I.T. Services. We will be with you as soon as an agent is available. Your patience is appreciated."

Tinny, saxophone-heavy Adult Contemporary music kicks in and out intermittently. You put in one earbud and try not to listen to the harsh sax oscillating through your tympanic membrane and into your brain.

If you wish to continue to hold, turn to **281**. If you would rather draft the Presentation without your Report, turn to **223**.

146

The Pay Centre Rep's phone is still going to voicemail. There goes your weekend, maybe your entire vacation. Or apartment. *Shit*. Lose 1 SKILL, 1 STAMINA, 1 LUCK, and 1 TIME. Turn to **51**.

147

You pull all the food out of your bag and throw pieces left and right to open a path (cross all the Provisions off your FRM-0001c). The geese attack the food like ravenous piranhas. You make a break for it before they can recover.

Turn to **112** but *halve* the STAMINA loss suffered, rounding up (because geese are pricks).

148

You jump in. "I think Eugene McCarthy said it best with, 'the only thing that saves us from the bureaucracy is its inefficiency.' "

"Yes, yes!" the A.D. says with a massive smile. "Inefficiency is precisely what I was going for." Those around the room nod like they were thinking the same thing. You silently thank I.B. Trivia Night for bailing you out of this one. Turn to **267**.

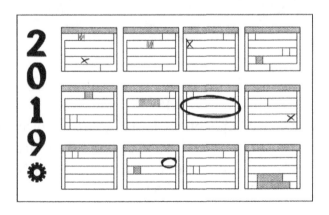

149

A Snack tumbles out of the recalcitrant Machine, and you snatch it up. You may eat it now or add it to your FRM-0001c for later.

Will you sit:

With some colleagues	Turn to **303**
By your lonesome	Turn to **144**

150

Your laptop slows to a crawl, its hard drive ticking over like a Geiger counter in a nuclear hot zone. A window full of DOS-prompt nonsense pops up. Your computer shuts down. Critical updates, nemesis of the time-pressured, strike again!

You're forced to languish through two more reboots. It finally finishes. You rattle in usernames and passwords like it's the Second Coming and your immortal soul is on the Shared Drive. Lose 1 TIME and turn to **381**.

151. A bright-eyed nurse leans into your field of view.

151

You come to in brightness and pain. Something's pushing on your chest and draped over your neck. Your arms and legs won't move. You focus blearily on a room full of beds, floor-to-ceiling curtains, and rhythmically beeping machines. A series of lines, pullies, and casts have turned you into a living construction site. You groan but it's only a dry, scratchy whisper. A perky, bright-eyed nurse in pastel purple scrubs leans into your field of view. "Welcome to the Land of the Living!" he says altogether too cheerfully.

"Nghuuuh," you reply.

"You'll be okay, the doctors fixed you up. You're lucky you weren't in the first car!"

Ah, sent to Traction courtesy of CityTranspo. You wonder if you can get that on a t-shirt and chuckle, then grimace as things not meant to grind do so with gusto.

"Meds wearing off? Don't worry, the doctor gave you the good stuff."

He fiddles with something out of your field of view. Whatever it is, it's good. It takes you to a fluffy cloud without worry or pain. Catastrophic accident victim? Who cares, not if you've got this stuff.

Ah, CityTranspo. It was only a matter of time before the C-Train went off the rails big-time. You chuckle again but there's no pain now. You're surprised an accident this bad hadn't happened before now. There can only be so many "minor derailments" before someone gets seriously hurt. Unfortunately, that someone is you. At least you weren't killed, or maybe that too is unfortunate. You're certainly going to think so when struggling to use your limbs and go to the bathroom again. Pain won't be a problem, though, not with your glorious new addiction. And look, an AMBULANCE-CHASING GHOUL is stalking your way. He's got the widest smile you've ever seen, one that says you'll never have to work again. Maybe that's just the Fentanyl.

You could turn to **Appendix 2: Performance Review** if you want, but maybe consider getting this adventure back on track by turning to **201** instead. I won't tell, it'll be our secret.

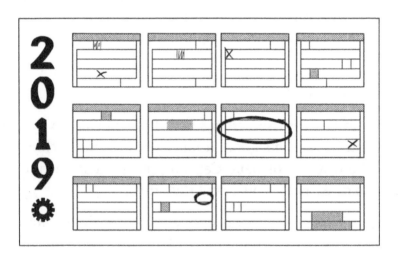

152

If you haven't already, what will you do next?

Brew a fresh pot of coffee	Turn to **292**
Boil water for a mug of tea	Turn to **270**
Check out the First-Aid Kit	Turn to **183**
Search the drawers and cabinets	Turn to **276**
Look in the fridge	Turn to **374**
Leave the kitchenette	Turn to **118**

153

He scratches his head. "It's basically just me down here. I asked for Central Stats's help."

"Who," you maintain.

"I'd have to ask my counterpart over there but he's not in the office this week." *Click, click. Click.*

Your faces twitches; lose 1 STAMINA.

You tell him, as calmly as possible, that he's going to help you fix this mess. Turn to **93**.

154

You head to your cubicle. "I thought you started vacation today," Ezra says from one cube over.

Yes, why not? You tell Ezra about your day; they shake their head. "Wow, who would send someone else's draft report to the A.D.? I could've helped but was stuck in meetings all morning." They look you up and down. "Hey, maybe I still can. You're about my size. I've got a nice suit, and its just back from the cleaners. Want it for your briefing?"

Your reply?

"Uh…yes!"	Turn to **385**
"Nah, that's alright."	Turn to **170**

155

"I'd be 300 pounds if I kept snacks at my desk. Some of us don't lose weight as easily as you," Barb says. Lose 1 STAMINA and turn to **253**.

156

You walk to the old, dirty, irregularly storied J.B. McGregor Building on the Citadel's south-east corner. One side of its concrete exterior is still rain-soaked, and its roof is a mass of metal ducts and tubing. The Department of Health must have some labs inside. You scrape open the building's crooked, steel, safety-glassed door and step inside.

Do you have an ID Badge or Temporary Pass? If so, turn to **193**. If not, turn to **233**.

157

"Just a minute, please!" you hear from across the floor. A large woman wrapped in a paisley shawl hurries toward you.

You panic, fumble the bar, and knock the whole box into her cubicle with a crash of hard chocolate on concrete. You flee like the thief you are. "Sorry!" you call over your shoulder, but you're only sorry you got caught.

Lose 1 MERIT and turn to **249**. No, you didn't get away with a Chocolate Bar. Jesus…

158

You cross your arms and bite your tongue. Lose 1 STAMINA and turn to **277**.

Your head hurts. That's your first thought as you come to. The second is how ridiculous you must look. A fit young man and woman, both in Lulu Lemon athleisure, stand over you, slack-jawed and wide-eyed. The man is already recording you on his phone.

You try to stand, sag against the wall, and smooth down your shirt.

"Uh, you want me to call an ambulance or something?" the man says, still recording.

"No, no, I'm good," you say. You hope you aren't drooling. You pull yourself upright and flail an arm at the door. "Washroom's flooded again."

The woman nods. "You sure you don't want—"

"No, s'okay." You push past them, shoes squelching with disgusting bathroom water.

You really should go to the hospital, and you can by turning to **344**, or you can try to carry on if you think you're made of sterner stuff. You are, however, very badly hurt. Lose 2 SKILL and 4 STAMINA. You should technically lose 1 LUCK as well, but why kick a concussed horse? You struggle upstairs. Lose 3 points of TIME and turn to **382**.

160

As your back goes into spasm for a third time, you and Sammi opt to leave. You sweep through the door, mentally willing Sadie to not say "namaste."

"Have a blissful afternoon," she says with a half bow.

Touché, Sadie. *Touché*. Your insides gurgle as they come to grips with the vegan undertaking thrust upon them, but you will only need to visit the washroom three more times before the day is out. Lose 4 TIME (3 for the meal, 1 for this afternoon's frequent washroom breaks).

Count your blessings for such a minor side effect, for you have withstood the dense and experimental fare of a VEGAN SADIST, whose quest to elevate subsistence foods knows no bounds. As you climb into the BMW, you're not certain you feel any healthier or more balanced, but you certainly feel fancy. Maybe the food worked after all. Turn to **6**.

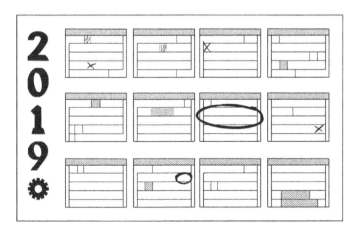

161. You scan the washroom but can't see anyth—a RAT!

161

You descend into the building's underbelly. You haven't been down here in months. The ceiling is low, the walls white blocks and drywall, and the floor is stained concrete. The air is damp and earthy. It's the kind of hallway you'd expect to find in a haunted asylum.

Rounding a corner, you make for the bathroom, giving the wall marked "Danger. Consult asbestos register prior to commencing work," a wide berth. A door down the hall leads to the grimy gym that reeks of sweat and rusty free-weights.

You enter the sunken washroom only to stumble into a fetid pool. You're standing in a good three inches of scummy bathroom water. Gross. Why can't they get this flooding under control? You freeze.

Something moved.

You scan the washroom but don't see anyth—a RAT! Its black fur is slick and matted, its beady eyes glistening in the fluorescents. It's swimming straight for you!

You yank open the door and trip on the step, careening across the hall and straight into the wall.

Test your Luck. If you're Lucky, turn to **331**. If you're Unlucky, turn to **315**.

Your bag catches a loose desk arm, making it rattle. Victor snorts awake. He gives you a Cheshire Cat grin. "How's the Report going?"

Oh, no! "Fine, Victor, but I've got—"

"That reminds me of that report we worked on when you were just getting started. Do you remember..."

It's begun: an endless stream of recall that won't end until you or he are dead. Your signals that this conversation must end are as clear as a fire alarm. Sadly, Victor is immune to such niceties. He rises, hands firmly pocketed, and edges along as you withdraw.

Resolve your Confrontation.

IDLE CHATTERER *SKILL* 7   *STAMINA* 6

Deduct 1 TIME for each *Confrontation Round* you lose. If you win or lose 3 TIME, turn to **369**. If Victor's endless barrage of anecdotes drains the last of your STAMINA, turn to **344**.

163

You don't need this. You've got a pile of work to get through before your vacation. You tell him to get out of the way and call him a lazy bum for good measure. Only, he doesn't just stand there and take your abuse.

There's no moral high ground here; resolve your Confrontation.

INDIGNANT VAGRANT   *SKILL* 10   *STAMINA* 4

You may Escape at any time by turning to **123**. If you "win," turn to **67**. If you lose, turn to **136**.

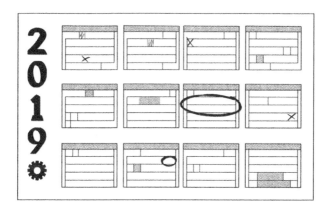

164

"Stuffed shirts'd forget your asses if you weren't sitting on 'em all day," he grumbles. He tugs open a drawer like it took half his pension and slaps a form on the desk. "Fill that out and give me some photo ID."

Lose 1 LUCK for the lie and turn to **66**.

165

The milk is sour and curdled. You gag, spitting it back into the carton; most of it, anyway. Lose 1 STAMINA. You check the date and it's just this side of expired.

"Ah, *luh-luh, c'est pourri, là?* It's bad? *Tabarnak,*" he says, taking the dripping carton.

He hands you a cup of hot coffee instead, which you use to wash the sourness from your mouth and the texture from your memory. He also gives you a free Cinnabonne (add it to your FRM-0001c).

"On the house," he says apologetically.

You fix your coffee how you like it and leave.

"*Pardon* once again and *bon aventure!*" he calls.

Lose 1 TIME and turn to **351**.

166

You totter around the birds, tiptoeing the last few yards then breaking into a run. Turn to **317**.

167

Barb counters your feeble attempts to disengage with whinging aplomb.

Resolve your Confrontation.

SHIFTLESS MOANER *SKILL* 8 *STAMINA* 8

If you win, turn to **195**. If you lose, turn to **344**.

168

You struggle to make sense of the madness. It takes a chunk of the morning and a portion of your sanity. The emails keep coming. There are too many requests to action, too many meetings on the horizon, and you need to dig around the Shared Drive for several files. You manage in the end but lose a part of yourself in the process. Lose 2 STAMINA and 2 TIME. Turn to **76**.

169

You head toward the washroom along the building's north side, gazing at the dark sky and back lawns. In the middle of the complex, the Tower rears into the sky. Its deep-set, concrete-framed windows and roof-mounted air-conditioning vents make it look like a giant, retro-futuristic bureaucratic battery. You thread a narrow Collaboration Area of blue pleather chairs with wobbly desk arms and hear a throaty snort. It's Victor asleep in a chair nearby.

Bent by the weight of a thousand government projects, Victor started with the Civil Service when he was just a kid. That had to be nearly forty years ago. Unwilling to retire, probably because his wife would murder him soon after, Victor has become an IDLE CHATTERER, a man capable of eroding productivity in a ten-foot, anecdote-riddled radius. If he wakes up...no, you don't want to think about it.

Test your Skill. If you're Successful, turn to **188**. If you're Unsuccessful, turn to **162**.

170

"Nah, that's okay—you just got it cleaned," you say.

"Okay, well, if you need some help this afternoon, just give me a call," Ezra says.

You thank them profusely. You need all the help you can get. Note down that Ezra can help you this afternoon and turn to **302**.

171

The line rings once, twice, and…SAX, louder than ever. Lose 1 STAMINA and 1 TIME. Will you maintain (turn to **189**) or give up on network support (turn to **223**)?

172

Roll one die. If it's a 6, you throw up in the nearest available receptacle (lose 2 STAMINA). If it's any other number, you manage to hold down your bile. In either event, rate your present stage of grief:

Denial	Turn to **180**
Anger	Turn to **392**
Bargaining	Turn to **54**
Depression	Turn to **275**
Acceptance	Turn to **7**

173

You hunt for signs of habitation. It looks like Basma and Ezra are in today. Ezra's a pretty good Junior Analyst. Basma's an excellent Co-Op Student who could go far, if the Civil Service doesn't strip her spirit like a bedbug-infested cubicle, that is.

You watch four people gather in the nearby Collaboration Space. They look famili—*crap*, it's the Central Governance Unit (C.G.U.). Your boss was supposed to meet them this morning. You once saw the C.G.U. take half an hour to scope out a thirty-minute meeting.

Will you:

Get their attention	Turn to **107**
Get down	Turn to **28**

174

You stand your ground like a British Redcoat set to receive the enemy. Barb draws near. You grimace at the smell of microwaved fish wafting along with her. "Hi, Barb," you say. Turn to **399**.

175

With one analyst gone, you back toward the stairwell, nodding at the other's incomprehensible jabber until you slip through the door. Turn to **161**.

176

Taylor laughs. "Bitch, you can't afford me!" You chuckle and walk back to your cube. Turn to **2**.

177

You cancel the briefing and get a giddy rush like you're careening down a rollercoaster's first drop. I get it. I really do. Maybe time got away from you, as it so often does, or your back was broken by burdensome bureaucracy. I can't fault you, that's your supervisor's job. *If* he ever returns. I wouldn't put money on it. Whatever the cause, you head for the station, running a mental checklist of people who could get you another job. But that's for another day. You have a vacation to start. God, you hope the trains are still running. Turn to **Appendix 2: Performance Review**.

178

You tell André your tale of woe. He nods solemnly. "*Toi et c'est magané, là?* The Civil Service is hard, no?" He blows a raspberry and shrugs. "Troubles come and go but at least you have André, and this—on the house." He slides you a coffee and Cinnabonne (add it to the Provisions box on your FRM-0001c).

You smile and thank him for his folksy wisdom and fried pastry. Restore 2 STAMINA but lose 2 TIME.

"*Bon aventure!*" André says as you leave. Turn to **351**.

Live

for

today

179. Sadie's depressingly upbeat.

179

Sadie's Vegan Charcuterie has the aesthetic of a fashion-forward police interrogation room. The lighting is pot-light-stark. Angular metal stools line a long counter and similarly uncomfortable-looking chairs surround IKEA-blonde tables. The seating looks like it will send your back into spasm in 0.32 seconds.

The cold, white walls are branded with inspirational phrases that make Nike's seem downright apathetic. A chalkboard menu lists colourful, optimistic sounding food at very pessimistic prices.

A woman in yoga pants and riding boots comes to your table. She's depressingly upbeat. "Hi, I'm Sadie! I hope you're having an uplifting day!"

You consider telling her about your day for precisely 0.32 seconds, which is when your back goes into spasm. You grimace and adjust your posture.

"You should take up yoga. I bet you're all bound up," she says, actually poking your belly. "I've got the perfect solution. Clean body, clean mind!"

Pick your poison:

Potent Juice Cleanse	Turn to **389**
Dynamic Juice Cleanse	Turn to **24**
Compelling Juice Cleanse	Turn to **59**

180

You shake your head in a futile effort to turn back time. "No. This can't be happening," you say to yourself.

She clears her throat. "I'm sorry, but this comes directly from the A.D."

"You don't understand—my boss is out of the office today. I've never briefed an A.D. I'm going on vacation tomorrow!"

"Yes, we're aware he's away. I think you're making too much of this."

"Too much? You *think*—I'm just a junior analyst, lady. I'm only acting!" You're starting to lose it, your weakened nerves cracking like a dropped cellphone screen.

Resolve your internal conflict as a Confrontation.

BURGEONING ANXIETY   *SKILL* 8   *STAMINA* 5

If you maintain, turn to **263**. If you lose it, turn to **344**.

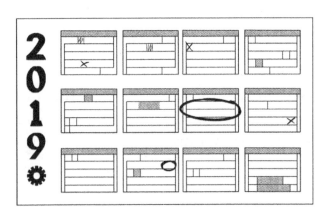

181

You bump into a co-worker and blush—it's your OF-FICE CRUSH (Unrequited). Their wind-tousled hair looks good, as does their slightly rumpled, tailored shirt. They grin, eyes sparkling. "Network's down. Must be the tenth time this month."

You chuckle and fuss with your rain-bedraggled hair. "At least it's Friday," you say timorously.

They smile, turning you to jelly. "Hey, can I borrow your pass real quick? I left mine at home and need to run to the sixth. I'll be right back," they add with a devilishly disarming grin.

Will you:

Refuse?	Turn to **245**
Hand it over?	Turn to **312**
Agree, but only if they:	
Lend you some Spare Change	Turn to **185**
Buy you a TabarSnak	Turn to **342**
Take you out for lunch	Turn to **99**

182

You throw the grinning trolls one last glare, hold your breath, and dart into their noxious cloud. You pull open the door and slip through, inhaling an asphyxiating wisp of smoke. Lose 1 STAMINA and turn to **265**.

183

You pop open the First Aid Kit. *Test your Luck*. If you're Lucky, turn to **239**. If you're Unlucky, turn to **362**.

184

Why? Why would you do such a thing? Not only is it animal cruelty (for some reason), but it's also plain and simple suicide. Have you seen Canada geese in action? I'm guessing you haven't, or you wouldn't be here.

The gaggle is on you immediately and in force. You try to fight then try to run but it's no use. You're peppered with hammering beaks and powerful body blows, several to the head, and you go down.

Smokers drop their butts and people crowd the Braddock Building's windows to watch the broiling mass of geese, wondering what could have stirred them to such violence. They get their answer as the geese withdraw, revealing your prone, bleeding, feather-covered body.

Are you still alive? Only the paramedics will know for sure. But your workday is certainly over. Turn to **344**.

185

You say you're broke and could use some Spare Change. "Ooh, sorry, I don't have any on me," they say, patting their clothes. They look at you expectantly.

Will you:

Refuse	Turn to **245**
Hand it over	Turn to **312**
Agree, but only if they:	
Buy you a TabarSnak	Turn to **342**
Take you out for lunch	Turn to **99**

186

You pull the copier away from the wall. Everything looks fine. You crouch down and jiggle the cord. That's the last thing you remember.

Waking up in an ambulance, you learn that something had chewed the power cord, exposing the wire. Which you were unfortunate enough to touch. Several defibrillator charges later and you were respiring once more, though your workday's far behind. Turn to **344**.

187

"Still sounds better than mine," she moans. Lose 1 STAMINA and turn to **253**.

188

You slink past Victor. He snorts and turns toward you. Your heart becomes a lead weight in your chest. His eyes are still closed. You hurry out of the Collaboration Area and sigh with relief, though not too loudly lest you wake him. Turn to **199**.

189

You drape the earbud's cord over your ear, holding it close each time the music drops and letting it dangle when the stinging sax resumes.

"An agent will be with you as soon as one is available. Please note we are experiencing a higher than normal call volume."

You fumble to disconnect before you can be thanked for your patience again. Like Elvis, it has left the building. Lose 1 STAMINA and 1 TIME. If you have any left (patience or time), turn to **223**.

190

Your memory gets...choppy after that. There's more drink and food, singing, cheering, something happening in a bathroom. Then you and Sammi (who seems totally fine, by the way) take an Uber back to the office. Sammi lives nearby, so it's no problem for them. You, though, are a total disaster. You end up leaning on a tree, the honking of geese echoing in your half-conscious brain while your building swirls before you. You don't normally drink so much. WHY did you drink so much? You can't finish your briefing in this state, let alone stand upright during it.

Sadly, you've fallen prey to the BACHANALEAN RESTERAUNTEUR, who's favourite customers are high-powered lawyers, crooked doctors, and weary civil servants. Your workday is at an end. Turn to **344**.

191

You clear the station and head deeper into the Citadel. The main walk is a long, straight shot into the heart of the complex. At the centre of it all resides the Tower: a brooding, thirty-storey sentinel of bureaucratic glory. Every senior manager worth their salt jockeys for an office inside. A massive flag on top whips wetly in the wind, a constant, flapping reminder of the people you serve. The area between you and the complex is an expanse of laneways, lawns, and parking lots. The best spots are already packed by people who pay top dollar to avoid CityTranspo's dangerously lacklustre service.

Someone calls to you. It's your Old Friend, Sammi, a Senior Analyst in I.G.A.B., your partner branch. They lock their BMW with a pert "honk-honk." You walk together, catching up on office politics along the way.

"Tough break about your Report," Sammi says. You frown, perplexed. "Your boss didn't tell you? Someone in C.P.D. (Central Policy Directorate) shared your Report with your Associate Deputy (A.D.)."

What? Your draft Report is bold, reaching—it's meant to spark discussion, not go up to senior management. The A.D.'s going to have questions. Hard, endless questions. You grab Sammi by the lapels. "It's not ready. I sent it to C.P.D. for comment, not A.D. review!"

"Hey, don't shoot the messenger. Look, this is your boss's problem. Just fob it off on him."

You mumble something noncommittal. How the hell did your Report end up in the A.D.'s Office (A.D.O.)? You don't have time for this. You have a desk to clear and a pay problem to resolve so you can pay your bills.

"Let's do lunch today, okay? I'm buying," Sammi says.

You decide Sammi's right; this *is* above your pay grade. It's the sort of mix-up for which Senior Policy Analysts were made. You'll dump the problem in your boss's lap and maybe even meet Sammi for lunch.

Yeah, everything will be okay.

Lose 1 TIME and note down that Sammi invited you to lunch. Turn to **13**.

192

You try to open your Report on the Shared Drive but it's *slow*. Probably fallout from the network outage. As soon as the folder populates with files you copy the Report to your desktop. Fool you once, network… Only, that too takes forever. Why did you add so many images? The vanity. Luckily, it doesn't crash once. You spend some time updating your Presentation. Add 1 to its version number and lose 2 TIME.

If the Presentation is version 2 and you'd like to give it a polish, turn to **226**. If it's version 4 or you're otherwise fine with it, turn to **103**.

193

You schlep to the seventh floor only to find the entire National Statistics Unit out to lunch. Literally. How utterly apropos for your day. You're going to have to power through without those stats. You stalk back to the office. Lose 1 STAMINA and 3 TIME. Turn to **323**.

194

You can't seem to get away. Barb keeps drawing you back with intense interjections, using the bonds of civility to hold you like a soul-sucking lasso of inescapable complaint.

If you haven't already, will you:

Offer to bring her a coffee	Turn to **119**
Brush her off and move along	Turn to **308**
Tell her about another job	Turn to **284**
Try something more aggressive	Turn to **167**

195

You go round and round with Barb until she's out of breath, which is when you beat a hasty retreat. Lose 2 TIME and turn to **208**.

196

You could write a polished presentation in your sleep, and probably have. This one's short, concise, and persuasive. Note Presentation v.4 in the Documents box of your FRM-0001c. Lose 1 STAMINA and 2 TIME and turn to **103**.

197

Where is it? No! You left your Folding Umbrella in the office after last week's storm (strike it off your FRM-0001c). Damn it, you're going to be soaked by the time you reach the office. It's going to be a very uncomfortable morning. Deduct 2 STAMINA. You press on. Turn to **330**.

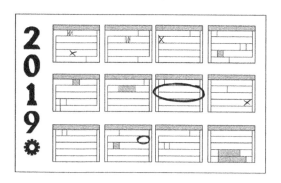

198

You wrestle the name out of Barb relatively quickly. "Joshua's in the C.P.D., not the I.A., whatever that is. He was working on your stats. He's so useless. I don't know how the C.P.D. gets so much funding when we do all the work. That's government for you. Why do things right when you can do them wrong a dozen times." She turns back to her monitor and continues to gripe.

Lose 1 STAMINA and 1 TIME. Note that Joshua has your stats and gain 1 LUCK for the info. You slip away while you can. Turn to **208**.

199. What has been seen cannot be unseen.

199

The washroom door's wood veneer is scratched and peeling. You push it open and step inside. Two forest green stalls, a cheap, marbled resin counter, and two old, chipped American Standard sinks are inside. Several plastic signs bearing crossed-out faucets and bold "Non-Potable Water" and "Do Not Drink" warnings are set on the counter. You didn't see an email about *another* boil water advisory. The nearest stall is out of order, so you throw open the next. You grimace but what's been seen cannot be unseen.

Someone has defiled the stall, gobbed and flecked it like an abattoir floor, only blood would have been less horrific.

You stagger back and flee the scene. Lose 1 STAMINA.

Where will you go?

Another washroom	Turn to **215**
Your cubicle	Turn to **376**

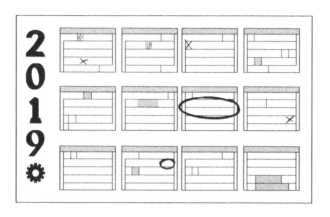

200

You fall into a fugue state, body dripping sweat as you shovel delicious taco into your mouth as fast as your throat will allow. It's so delicious and *hot*, yet you can't stop eating. You finish your meal, licking your fingers and even the wrapper to get every bit of sauce. Restore 1 STAMINA for each taco you ate.

Rejoice, for you have survived an ARDENT COOK, whose fiery and flavoursome fare has overwhelmed many a diner. Your tolerance is irrelevant, Mary knows it and will push you to vistas of heat and flavour beyond your wildest imaginings.

High on endorphins, you and Sammi return to the BMW and loosen your sweat-soaked clothes. Lose 3 TIME and turn to **6**.

201

The C-train pulls into Darby Station, a retro-modern building of glass, concrete, and harsh fluorescents. Its riveted steel roof slopes into the sky with the futurism of a V-1 rocket's launch ramp. The train grinds to a halt and its doors open, spilling passengers onto the platform. It reeks of urine. Why does this station always smell like a latrine? Because someone used it as a toilet, that's why.

Your mind turns from public micturition to the tasks ahead. It being a holiday Friday means fewer bodies to do the usual amount of work. Only sad sacks, workaholics, and bureaucratic casualties will be in today. You hope it's quiet so you can clear your desk, and maybe, just maybe, cut out a bit early. You've just got to work out your pay issue, wrap up a couple long overdue projects, and turn on your out-of-office replies. It should be an easy day.

You go up the concrete steps two at a time. An obelisk of an informational display indicates that your train is fifteen minutes behind schedule. How a couple railed cars on a single line can run behind schedule is beyond you. At least you weren't in another derailment. Lose 1 TIME.

How do you want to get to the office?

The side lot, your usual shortcut Turn to **225**
The main exit and long way around Turn to **375**

202

You get laughs from the room and over the speaker. Even the D.H. is chuckling. Wait, they think you're joking! Lose 1 STAMINA and 1 LUCK for the existential body blow. Turn to **277**.

You jog up to the fourth floor. It's alarmingly open concept. The only cubicles are along the distant exterior windows. Even then, their foot-high walls wouldn't safeguard a bit of Protected gossip let alone a Classified document. The rest of the floor is filled with conversational touch-down areas, hot desks, and conference tables. Skeletal support columns loom over everything. Sure, the scant sky-blue walls and bright pleather furniture are cheery, but you could hear a screw drop out of a keyboard tray across the floor. Which you would be hearing if the floor wasn't deserted. *Odd.*

You shrug and follow one of the few walls around to the washroom. It's way nicer than yours. The stalls are minty green and its white tiles very Subway Chic. You enter a stall, set down your bag (I suppose hooks would ruin the clean lines of the door), and get down to business.

The washroom's outer door creaks open. "Hello?" a man says.

You go as rigid as a tax audit. "Yes?"

"I thought everyone was working from home today," he says. That explains the OfficePlace 3.0 Graveyard outside. You ask him what he means. "Well, the bedbugs."

Bedbugs? *Bedbugs!* You look around the stall expecting a scene from a bug-themed horror film, but there's nothing. Your bag! You snatch it off the floor and hug it to your body. *But that's where they'd be!* You throw it on the ground and sit paralyzed, feet off the floor and arms raised.

"You just finish up and come on out," he says. The door closes.

You complete your ablutions and, scratching at hundreds of invisible bugs, step outside. A paunchy Orkin man in khakis and a white hard hat is standing at a respectful distance. He's holding the leash of a beagle wearing a harness. It'd be the cutest thing ever in any other situation.

"Yeah, they found a dead bedbug in there yesterday," he says. The bugs nibbling your skin multiply by a factor of two. You vaguely recall an email about bedbugs, but they're so regular they've become routine. "We'll just let old Rusty give you a snuffle. Scootch, Rusty."

Rusty trots over, ears flopping adorably, and sniffs your shoes and bag.

"You're probably fine if—"

"Ruf," Rusty says, pawing at your bag.

The Orkin Man scratches his head under his hardhat. "Bad luck. Got any spare clothes? I wouldn't go home until we can…" You don't hear the rest of his sentence through the screaming in your mind. It goes without saying that your workday is at an end. Turn to **344**.

204

"Sorry, this food dies with me," you say, scurrying away. You grin at Taylor's indignant howl. They'll get over it. You head back to your cubicle. Lose 1 TIME and turn to **2**.

205

You wander toward your building, your mind oscillating between your impending vacation, imminent briefing, and the jerk who sent your Report to the A.D. You sigh, then stop, and keep very, very still.

You've wandered into a massive gaggle of sleeping Canada geese. Their long necks are tucked back into their bodies as they nap on the wet pavement in the afternoon heat. You're far from the Citadel and miles from help, not that anyone could save you if these CO-BRA-CHICKENS wake up.

What will you do?

Punt one like a football	Turn to **184**
Dash through the fearsome fowl	Turn to **333**
Pick your way through the minefield	Turn to **274**

206

If you no longer have your ID Badge, turn to **386**. If you do have your ID Badge, how will you spend your precious lunch hour?

In the cafeteria   Turn to **5**
At your desk   Turn to **110**
With Sammi (if you saw them earlier) Turn to **122**
Searching the third floor for food   Turn to **356**

207

A bit of warmth drains from Drew's voice. "Yeah, I thought so—the H.R. side isn't jiving with the pay side."

You rest your head in your hand. It was a mistake to take this acting assignment. All it earned you is a stop in pay and a raise in workload. You'll never make that mistake again.

"I've started the paperwork for emergency pay. You should get it in two days," he says.

It'll mean the same problem in two weeks and tax problems down the road, but at least you can eat and pay rent. You thank him for doing what he could. Lose 1 TIME and 1 LUCK.

Note down that you got paid and turn to **341**.

208. *Even with all that vileness, the sink takes the trophy.*

You pass through one of the plusher Collaboration Areas. A Flexible Worker, lacking an assigned desk, is trying to work at a stand-only touch-down station. It looks difficult with three people jabbering loudly at the table outside the kitchenette. You hurry inside.

It's not much of a kitchenette with only a scant foot of waterlogged counter space. The adjacent fridge bears an oft-ignored cleaning schedule and a wiener that someone's taped to the door. The wiener is more puffball mould than meat product; you wouldn't have believed it could go mouldy, but the evidence is dangling before you. Not to be outdone, the microwave door is open, revealing an interior spattered with the desiccated remains of every sauce and casserole known to humanity.

Even with all that vileness, the small, metal sink takes the trophy for "Most Horrible of Sights." It's filled with dirty dishes left by the Soak-It-and-Forget-It Brigade, their soggy leftovers floating in dingy dishwater like so many swollen corpses. A filthy sponge that has soaked up more horror than a crime scene investigator is perched on the faucet housing beside a bottle of watered-down dish detergent.

The entire kitchen is in clear violation of the wrinkled "you're Mother doesn't work here! (*sic*)" printout aggressively taped to the backsplash.

The walls are festooned with notices of work events, for-sale posters, and a small First-Aid Kit. A side table half blocking the fridge bears a stained coffee-maker full of yesterday's coffee, an electric kettle, and a very stained stainless-steel toaster.

How do you proceed?

Brew a fresh pot of coffee	Turn to **292**
Boil water for a mug of tea	Turn to **270**
Check out the First-Aid Kit	Turn to **183**
Search the drawers and cabinets	Turn to **276**
Look in the fridge	Turn to **374**
Flee the scene	Turn to **118**

209

"Hell, what good are you then? *Bye!*" Taylor says with finality. You shake your head and head to your cubicle. Turn to **2**.

210

"Thanks, this'll help," he says with a yellow smile. "You know the side lot's all fenced off, eh? Crews kept Rufus and me up all night." You look outside. Sure enough, construction fencing and corrugated metal storage units block the way to your building. You thank him and move along. Lose 1 TIME.

You've made an ally on the fringes of the Citadel. Note his dog's name, Rufus, for later.

Which way will you go?

The main exit and long way   Turn to **375**
Carry on and hope   Turn to **361**

211

"I was very impressed by your report—so bold and reaching," Faye says, sipping some wine. "I do have some questions, though. I felt the broader implications of such a massive streamlining were under analyzed."

You nod. "I forwarded it to C.P.D. for comment. They sent it to your office by mistake."

"Ah, that explains it. Things tend to get watered down before they cross my desk. The idea of a flatter organization, of letting programs innovate and experiment more freely, intrigues me. Why don't you run through your presentation?"

Yes, but did you draft a presentation?

Pfft, no   Turn to **336**
Of course!   Turn to **53**

212

If you've already drafted a presentation for the A.D., turn to **262**. If not, turn to **279**.

You fish the Briefing Material out of your damp bag and toss it on the file-and-forget pile (cross it off your FRM-0001c). Opening your small stationary cabinet, it promptly bangs into the drawer of the security cabinet. You close the security cabinet, wheel your chair out of the cubicle, open the stationary cabinet, and grab what you need.

Rolling your chair back into your office, you smash aside the keyboard tray and reopen the security cabinet. It doesn't budge. You must have bumped the dial when it closed, relocking it. You spin to reset, turn it this way, that way, and the other way, back to zero, push and…nothing. *Sigh*. Spin to reset, turn it this way, that way, and the other way, back to zero, push and…*ka-chunk*.

Keeping your kneecap out of harm's way, you reopen the cabinet, scrawl a note to your future self, stick it to the briefing material, close the drawer, spin around, and knock over your tiny garbage can. After wrestling your laptop onto its broken docking station, it powers up with a groan of struggling processors.

You sit back, your chair's dusty springs squeaking forlornly. The dry air, acetic with whatever they use to kill the Legionnaires, is making your throat scratchy. Lose 1 STAMINA. Despite the air, you're already starving. If you have Provisions, you may eat some while you get settled. Regardless, lose 1 TIME and turn to **352**.

214

You're heading for the basement when two analysts from another department round the corner. You met them at a policy development conference. Where Fin is short and balding, Fran is tall with wild, unkempt hair. You can never understand a thing they're saying, their Administrative Lingo being alien to yours.

"How's your I.B. Report? Did D.O. forward it to C.P.D. like you wanted?" Fran says, standing to your left.

Fin stands on your right and shakes your hand. "Our F.R. denied our request to J.V. our T.P. for the D.G. Can you believe it?"

"It's going to scuttle the P.M.'s C.P. Our D.G.'s going to L.H.S." Fran adds.

You nod. It's all you can do. What the hell are they saying? You'd run, but they've got you literally against the wall.

Resolve your Confrontation to escape these JABBER-ING ANALYSTS, losing 1 TIME each time you lose a *Confrontation Round*.

	SKILL	STAMINA
First ANALYST (FIN)	6	6
Second ANALYST (FRAN)	8	4

If you defeat both, turn to **175**. If they drive you to madness, turn to **344**. If you run Out of Time, turn to **92**.

215

You flee, glancing behind like whoever murdered that stall is coming for you next. You reach the stairwell's heavy fire door and crash through.

To which floor?

2nd Floor	Turn to **240**
4th Floor	Turn to **203**
Basement	Turn to **161**

216

You flick the console switch on and off. No joy.

Will you:

Hunt for the main switch	Turn to **237**
Check the power cord	Turn to **186**

217

His rheumy eyes widen. "Name and Personal Identifier?" You give him both, and he jots them down. "Big security violation, there. Gonna have to cite you and notify your supervisor, but thanks for your honesty," he adds with bitterest sarcasm. Lose 1 MERIT.

He slaps a form on the desk. "Fill that out and give me some photo ID." Turn to **66**.

218

"More!" you cry, pushing aside your empty plates and glasses. The last thing you want to do is go back to the grey, horrible Citadel. Not yet.

"That's the spirit," Tully cheers, heading around the counter. He brings you more wine (it looks like six ounces this time) and starts more pizza. You destroy the second round even faster than the first. Restore 2 STAMINA but lose 1 TIME.

Tully comes back with a mischievous grin. "I've got just the thing for you two—something special I've been cooking up. Interested?"

If you indulge, turn to **286**. If you resist, turn to **324**.

219

Test your Skill. If you're Successful, turn to **148**. If you're Unsuccessful, turn to **231**.

220

You make your play, deking left and right like a quarterback at the five-yard line.

Test your Skill. If you're Successful, turn to **396**. If you're Unsuccessful, turn to **100**.

221

"Hah! See, that's why I like you," Taylor chirps. "Hey, got any food? I'm famished."

Do you?

No	Turn to **209**
Yes, but no	Turn to **298**
Yes, and share it	Turn to **278**

222

You take the full brunt of Barb's whinging before wrestling the name out of her. "Joshua in the C.P.D. was working on that Appendix. He's so useless. I don't know how the C.P.D. gets so much funding when we do all the work. That's government for you—why do things right when you can do them wrong a dozen times." She limps onward, griping all the way to her desk. You head the other way. Lose 2 STAMINA and 2 TIME.

Note down that Joshua has your stats and restore 1 LUCK for the info. Turn to **154**.

223

You open PowerPoint and get to work on the Presentation. *Test your Skill*. If you're Successful, turn to **346**. If you're Unsuccessful, turn to **117**.

224

You take a brownie and give it a sniff. It smells like a chocolate brownie. You pop it in your mouth. It *is* a chocolate brownie! Restore 2 STAMINA.

You may eat another now, restoring 2 more STAMINA, or wrap it in a napkin for later (note it and its STAMINA gain on your FRM-0001c). You may also take Napkins if you wish. Turn to **35**.

225. *A dishevelled man blocks your path.*

You make for the side exit. A dishevelled man wearing three coats, fingerless gloves, and a touque blocks your path. You've seen him around the Citadel for years but have always managed to dodge him.

He holds out his filthy palm. "Spare some change? I just gotta catch the next train."

His sleeping bag and dirty, half-blind mutt are on the sidewalk outside. He isn't going anywhere.

How do you respond?

Brush by him and out the door	Turn to **291**
Hand over your Pocket Change	Turn to **327**
Offer him your Sad Bagged Lunch	Turn to **16**
Give him a piece of your mind	Turn to **163**

IAIGAD.

2019 A.D. Award
for Excellence

226

You need to jazz up this Presentation but are too close to it for an effective edit. Maybe someone can help? If anyone offered to help you this afternoon, look them up in **Appendix 1: Electronic Directory Services**. If not, turn to **103**.

227

Barb grimaces. "Must be, judging by the state of your hair. I wish I had hair as nice as yours. Mine's so thin."

You scowl and fuss with your hair. Lose 1 STAMINA and turn to **194**.

You shrug. "If that's the direction you want to take, no problem."

"Well…good," Sue says.

"Only, our unit's stretched pretty thin, so we'll have to hand it back to you."

Sue blinks. "But we don't have the capacity for—"

"I know, but we'll have to meet with Central Stats, find numbers that might support your angle, do a rewrite."

"No, I—"

"You're the subject matter expert, right?"

"Yes, but—" Sue hovers hesitantly as you walk away. Someone exits the elevators and pushes by her.

"You must have all the relevant data—you don't even need us," you say, leaving her behind.

You've outmaneuvered a MICRO-MANAGER. No small feat. Restore 1 LUCK but lose 1 STAMINA and 1 TIME (yes, just the one). You head back to your cubicle. Turn to **2**.

229

You sit at a red, paint-chipped picnic table, drink at the ready. You've tried every hot sauce there is and tear through baskets of suicide wings, no sweat. You're sure you can handle this. Can you?

Roll two dice and add 1 for each taco you ordered. If the total is *less than or equal to* your current STAMINA, turn to **69**. If the total is *greater than* your current STAMINA, turn to **200**. If the total is *double* your current STAMINA or double sixes, turn to **94**.

230

You plant your hands on his desk. "Why did you send my *draft* Report to the A.D.?"

He glances your way. "My A.D. wanted to see it, so I sent it along. Why?" *Click, click.*

"Because now *I've* got to do the briefing." *Ass.*

"Where do you work again?" *Click.* You remind him. Slowly. Painfully. "Oh, I thought it came from another department."

This guy is a policy manager? He doesn't even know his own department. Lose 1 STAMINA.

Click, click. "Why do you have to brief my A.D.?"

"Our A.D.," you correct him. "You tell me."

Click. "Our A.D.? You're not in my directorate," he says, finally minimizing his game. He scrolls through an Outlook inbox deeper than the Laurentian Abyssal. "Yeah, looks like I forwarded it to the wrong A.D. Associate Deputy, Assistant Director—so easy to confuse."

Wow. Just wow. Two years of work goes sideways because a hopeless manager of a unit that shouldn't exist sends an email to the wrong senior manager. Lose another STAMINA point.

Will you:

Get your stats from him (if necessary)	Turn to **153**
Tell him to fix this mess	Turn to **93**
Beat him to a bloody pulp	Turn to **236**
Give up on the turkey	Turn to **343**

231

"Meetings!" you drone, eliciting nervous laughter.

"Okay, we've got a comedian in N.H.Q.," the D.H. says. "Really, what comes to mind?"

Lose 1 STAMINA and your will to live. Turn to **267**.

232

Shit, shit, shit. "Uh… that's something my boss would handle. You sh—"

She clears her throat. "I'm afraid he's out of the office today. Didn't he tell you?"

What?! Why didn't he send you an email, leave a voicemail—anything? What a dick! Worse, he's been acting for *his* boss, your director, who was seconded to another department a month ago. God, that means you're in charge of this mess. A chill runs through your body. Lose 2 STAMINA and turn to **172**.

233

You can't get past the security barricade, and the person you've come to see isn't answering their phone (naturally). You try to get a temporary pass at the Security Office, but the desk officer is away and won't be back for a while. You don't have time to wait around. You'd slip through the security gates but a suspicious officer at the Security Kiosk is watching you like a hawk.

Nothing for it, you head back empty handed. Lose 2 STAMINA and 2 TIME. Turn to **323**.

234. *"Yes?" he grunts.*

234

You enter the cramped Security Office. Two cubicles behind the counter are piled with papers and junk. Sitting before you is a grizzled old Security Officer. He's sporting at least two days of salt-and-pepper stubble with plenty of nose and ear hair to keep it company. His natural habitat must be a dingy sports bar, his diet nothing but Crown Royal and unfiltered cigarettes.

"Yes?" he grunts, looking at you with brutal expectancy. The nicotine in his veins is clearly running thin.

Will you tell him your ID Badge is:

Lost	Turn to **96**
Loaned	Turn to **217**
At home	Turn to **164**

235

You go round and round with Barb until she's out of breath. That's when you beat a hasty retreat. Lose 2 TIME and turn to **154**.

236

You fly over his desk like a crazed mongoose, scrabbling as you both crash to the floor. I won't go into detail because I don't want to promote violence in the workplace, but let's just say his mouse is involved. As are the police, who haul you away after a good tasing.

One out of necessity, six for retribution.

Obviously, attacking him was the wrong choice. I only hope it was worth it. Was it? No, don't tell me. Your workday is at an end. Turn to **344**.

237

You hunt for the power switch, find it on the back, and give it a couple flicks. Rejoice! The printer boots up.

"It's still not printing," Adam says forlornly.

You check the display; it's reporting a lack of letter-sized paper. Looking in the cupboards, you find only torn, empty packages and stacks of misprints. *The lazy mother—* You remember seeing extra paper in the Supply Closet, but do you have the key? If so, turn to the reference written on it now.

If you don't have the key, you can only hope Adam finds paper elsewhere. Lose 1 TIME and turn to **51**.

238

Your work cell rings, and you answer. It's the A.D.'s Executive Assistant. You've been dreading this since running into Sammi. As expected, there are questions.

"My Report isn't finalized. C.P.D. sent it in error," you tell her.

"I'm sorry, the A.D. has already read your Report and wants a briefing this afternoon," she says.

"I really d— Did you say briefing?"

"We've scheduled you for late this afternoon. We'll need your materials in advance. I'll send an official tasking to your unit."

Your stomach drops.

Did you go to your boss's cube this morning? If so, turn to **340**. If not, turn to **232**.

239

You find one lonely Band-Aid among several torn, empty sleeves. If you suffer a physical injury (cut, bump or scrape), you can use it to restore 2 STAMINA. Use it now or mark it on your FRM-0001c, noting its STAMINA bonus. Unlike the other lazy jerks, you'll be sure to get the kit refilled. Turn to **152**.

240

You rattle down the steps, hurtling around each landing like a drift car, and yank open the third-floor fire door. The hallway down here is mint green, its carpet coarse and dark brown. The outer wall is lined with heavy, mag-locked doors that scream "go away." That only heightens your curiosity. If they had windows you'd be peering inside. At least the washrooms aren't locked. You creep down the hall and step inside.

This washroom's much nicer than yours. It has the same outdated fixtures and colours, only clean and in working order. The sinks aren't chipped, the faucets flow with hot *and* cold water, and the mirrors are delightfully unscratched. Luxury.

You get down to business, taking your time to wash and sort yourself out. Good thing, you were a mess. Restore 1 SKILL and 2 STAMINA.

Refreshed, you leave this astonishingly functional floor and make for your cubicle. Lose 1 TIME and turn to **14**.

241

You wing the cupcake at the goose, napkin and all. The confection bounces off her chest and onto the ground. The monster dips her head and, without breaking eye contact, swallows it whole. You have only increased her power.

What will you do next?

Charge   Turn to **100**
Try to get around   Turn to **220**
Deploy dinnerware (if you have any) Turn to **32**

242

You return to your desk and run through your Presentation one last time. You're about to correct some errors when the fire alarm's fierce blare fills the air. The damn thing's been going off every week for months; something to do with the construction outside. People throw up their hands in exasperation but collect their things and make for the stairs.

Do you? None of the floor wardens are in today and this is your last chance to perfect this Presentation. If you want to stay and finish, turn to **44**. If you'd rather send the A.D.O. what you've got and exit the building, turn to **87**.

243

You charge the smug Machine with your shoulder, rocking it onto its back legs. You dislodge THREE of your favourite candies! Only, like a dwarven king lusting after mithril, you have dug too greedily and too deep. And the Machine knows it. It falls back onto its front legs, delivering a shattering blow to your forehead. Glass goes everywhere. You go down, dazed and sprawling on the floor. The Machine teeters forward dangerously, looming over you like a steel demon from another age. It throws its bulk onto your cringing, screeching form. More glass breaks, metal clangs, something squishes.

Are you still alive? Only the paramedics will know for

sure. One thing's certain: your workday is over. Turn to **344**.

244

You search the Desktop and Recycle Bin for your Report but come up empty. You were sure you had a copy there. *Shit*. Without access to email or Shared Drive you won't have a copy of your Report on which to base your presentation.

Will you:

Call I.T. for help	Turn to **145**
Do your best from memory	Turn to **223**

245

"Ooh, sorry, can't. I'll be doing a lot of running around this afternoon. And it is technically a security violation," you say. No technically about it—it *is* a security violation.

Their face falls, taking your stomach along for the ride. "That's okay, I'll find someone else." They draw away.

"Go get a temporary pass—" you start, but they've already sauntered out of earshot. You did the right thing, but the snub still hurts. The sexy sleaze. Lose 1 STAMINA and turn to **332**.

246

You've been down this Shared Drive road before. It's a long, twisty road to nowhere. You tell Grant where you think you last saw the file and wish him luck. He's going to need it. Turn to **114**.

247

If you have any Provisions, you may eat a meal before getting up (lose 1 TIME if you do). If you want to hit the washroom to fix yourself up (you're probably a mess after your commute), turn to **124**. If you'd rather try to find food and some coffee or tea in the kitchenette, turn to **288**.

248

You dart through the crowd and hop up and along the edge of a planter like a Government-Appointed Ninja. Bypassing the logjam, you hurry to freedom. Turn to **191**.

249

You walk by a table bearing a paper plate of what looks like chocolate brownies. If you would like to try one, turn to **224**. If you'd rather not, turn to **35**. Whatever you choose to do, you may grab some napkins (add them to your FRM-0001c if you do).

250

You inform the A.D.O. that, due to heavy workload, no materials are forthcoming but that you'll proceed with the briefing. You take a couple laps of the campus outside before heading for the Tower. Turn to **313**.

251

You have defeated the rabid bat, either by trapping it in the bathroom or bludgeoning it to death with the keyboard. Either way, the commotion has attracted the A.D.'s Executive Assistant. She's standing in the doorway with a horrified look on her face.

"Bat," you say, breathing heavily. You drop the keyboard and straighten your outfit.

She nods. "Right this way." Turn to **139**.

252

There isn't time to ask Basma about your boss's note; ask again after the meeting. Return to **272**.

253

You can't seem to escape. Barb keeps drawing you back with intense interjections, using the bonds of civility to hold you.

If you haven't already, will you:

Ask her how her morning was	Turn to **140**
Brush her off and move along	Turn to **132**
Ask if she has any spare snacks	Turn to **155**
Try something more aggressive	Turn to **75**

254

Has anyone offered to help you out this afternoon (and hasn't already)? If so, note down this passage and look them up in **Appendix 1: Electronic Directory Service**.

If no one can help you, what will you do?

Start your review	Turn to **62**
Blow it off	Turn to **111**

255

"Wonderful, I love it!" she says.

Your heart soars. This could result in so many efficiencies. Lower delegated authorities and more responsive and accountable management would give frontline workers, and the public, everything they require. "I have plenty of ideas on how to implement this…" You trail off. The A.D. looks confused. "Is something wrong?"

Turn to **400** for your answer.

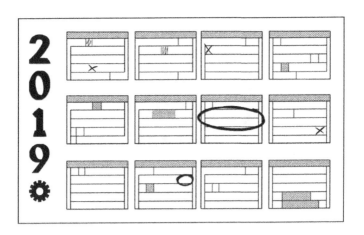

256

You forward Ezra the tasking. They respond immediately and are more than happy to help. Ezra's a natural at this sort of thing, and you know they'll do a fantastic job. You thank them profusely. Ezra wishes you luck with your briefing. Regain 1 LUCK and turn to **3**.

257

If you think you have time, you may go for a quick walk to clear your head (turn to **72**). If you'd rather get on with the day, turn to **282**.

258

You have a nice, quiet climb to the third floor. Regain 1 STAMINA for the exercise. Shouldering your way through the fire door (*ka-chunk*), you make your way into a maze of low, grey cubicles. Turn to **125**.

259. A needlessly cryptic note.

259

You stop by your boss's cube, but he isn't in yet. Typical. Leaning in, you find it piled with stacks of papers, notebooks, clothes, and bags. It looks like he was swept away by a policy whirlwind. You're about to leave when you notice a sticky note on the pad. It's addressed to you and is needlessly cryptic:

"Ask J in I.A. about the stats for your Report in A.D.O., B knows where. Happy Trails! –J"

You sigh. He can write "Happy Trails" but not the important bits? What the hell is "I.A."? Innovation Affairs? Internal Affairs? Internal Audit? International Affairs? Is it an office, unit, branch, or department? You can think of a dozen B's working in several units.

You don't have time to decipher his note right now. Add it to the Documents box on your FRM-0001c.

When encountering anyone whose name begins with "B," you can ask them about this note by subtracting 20 from the entry where they first speak to you (e.g. if at entry 120, turn to 100). If the new passage makes sense, you've found your answer. Make a note of this and restore 1 LUCK for the intel.

You spot a bit of Spare Change on his desk. He does owe you a coffee. If you want to grab it, add the Spare Change (or "x2" if you already have some) to your FRM-0001c. Turn to **378**.

260

Test your Skill. If you're Successful, turn to **86**. If you're Unsuccessful, turn to **71**.

261

You head to the recently cleaned washroom and freshen up. Looking in the worn, old mirror, you give yourself a pep talk. It actually works. Regain 1 SKILL and 1 STAMINA. Feeling better, you return to your desk. Turn to **395**.

262

If your Presentation is version 1 or 3, turn to **192**. If it's version 2, turn to **226**. If it's version 4, turn to **103**.

263

Nature loads the gun and circumstance pulls the trigger; you just dodged a bullet. "I'm sorry, I really need this vacation. It's already been a bit of a day," you say.

"I understand, we have a lot of those days in A.D.O. Look, I can push your materials deadline a bit, but that's all. Once the A.D. sets her mind on something there's no changing it."

"Can I ask how my Report ended up in A.D.O.?"

"The Director's Office in the C.P.D. sent it up for comment. It came from their generic email account, though, so it could have been anyone."

Great. "Well, thanks anyway."

"Okay, you hang in there. I'll send the meeting invitation now," she says.

Turn to **73**.

264

Test your Skill. If you're Successful, turn to **309**. If you're Unsuccessful, turn to **384**.

265

You cross the black marble foyer, pausing to scan your badge at the brushed steel security gate. It beeps affirmatively, the fingerprint-smeared plexiglass parting with a weighty clunk. You're hurrying toward the elevators when the sweet aroma of warm cinnamon buns hits you like a delicious wave. Of course, it's Cinnabonne Friday! Your stomach twists into a knot of hunger.

Over a glass door at the end of the hall, "TabarSnak" is written in cheap, red neon, the "S" blinking irregularly with an electric buzz. It calls to you like a voltaic street barker promising electric sex. Owned by André Gatineau, a delightfully irreverent Franco-Canadian from the wilds of Québec (KAY-BECK, not KWUH-BECK), the TabarSnak furnishes groggy, overworked civil servants with enough caffeinated fluid and calorie-rich solids to get through the day. The colourfully penned whiteboard out front advertises a coffee and Cinnabonne for just north of $2.

If you wish to indulge, turn to **297**. If you'd rather take the next elevator to your office, turn to **30**. Alternately, you could take the stairs by turning to **258**.

266

You bludgeon the goose with your bag. The corner of the laptop inside, so accustomed to your flesh and bone, batters the goose's skull. It goes down! You stand over your dazed adversary on the soggy field of victory and loose an exhilarated scream into the overcast sky. You're pretty sure it's illegal to batter Canada geese, but you don't care. Let the police come. Any charge, any fine would be worth the thrill of finally paying back one of these thugs of the lawn.

You fall back as its mate waddles toward you hissing malice. One goose was enough. You have already won a lifetime of glory. Every civil servant in the Citadel will sing of this day for fiscal years to come and at least two governments. Unfortunately, the Civil Service will not share your colleagues' acclaim; quite the opposite—lose 1 MERIT and 1 TIME. Turn to **397**.

267

You zone out as well-meaning people make well-meaning but totally impractical suggestions in very up-beat terms. The meeting goes on forever. At the end, it's agreed that action should be taken but that further discussion is necessary at the branch and regional level. After all, there are a lot of nuances between levels and regions. All of which should be categorized and classified, maybe by shade of colour in a heat map for the Committee's Action Plan.

The Forward Agenda is updated, the Minutes will be circulated (comments due by close of business, Tuesday). The next meeting is set for August. It's suggested that it be pushed to September due to summer vacation. Everyone agrees.

Lose 2 STAMINA and 3 TIME. If you're not Out of Time, you head to your office. Finally. Turn to **40**.

268

You show Barb your boss's note and ask if she knows anything about "J." She grimaces. "Your boss's writing is terrible, not that he has an excuse. My carpal tunnel's been acting up all week." You press her on the note.

Test your Skill. If you're Successful, turn to **198**. If you're Unsuccessful, turn to **42**.

269

You creep around another unit's territory and spot your target: chocolate bars, nine o'clock level. Slinking around the corner, you draw up to the cube. Fat, full-sized chocolate bars are neatly stacked in a cut-down box on a narrow counter on the cubicle. "Support My Daughter's Band. $2/bar," is written in sharpie on a card tucked inside. A small, slotted box wrapped in gold musical instrument paper sits beside it. The cubicle is plastered with at least a thousand photos of the occupant's Daughter Through the Ages.

If you have any Spare Change, you may buy a Chocolate Bar by turning to **27**. If for whatever reason you'd rather steal a bar, turn to **326**. If you'd rather leave them and press on, turn to **249**.

270

You set the half-filled electric kettle boiling. Pulling open the bare cabinets, you grab a chipped mug and old packet of Red Rose Tea. You pour a cup and, once it's steeped to your liking, take a sip. The hot liquid soothes your scratchy throat. Restore 1 STAMINA but lose 1 TIME. Turn to **152**.

271. *A trio of hunched, crabby-looking civil servants.*

271

A trio of hunched, crabby-looking civil servants are puffing away under a No Smoking sign by the entrance. One's smoking a cigarette, another a cigar, and the last a vape pen. They're wearing hooded raincoats and grumbling about the weather, their lives, and how things would be better if they were in charge. Sheltered in the lee of the building, their bilious cloud of bile, smoke, and black cherry vapour has coalesced in front of the entrance.

You give them a glare with a pointed glance at the sign. The CHAIN-SMOKING TROLLS note your indignation but stand firm.

Will you:

Politely ask them to move	Turn to **104**
Let them have it	Turn to **26**
Dash through the cloud and inside	Turn to **182**

272

You sit, keeping the busted chair against the wall to avoid flying backwards. No need to add a concussion to your to-do list. "What seems to be the problem?" you ask.

Dominic snorts. He doesn't care for your boss's "so-called innovations" regarding his governmental stake-holders. It's not your file, and Basma's been assisting your boss. For all you know, harassment aside, Dominic has a legitimate issue (even if he's being an ass).

You suggest that your units sit down to discuss things as a group. He baulks. You try fobbing him off on your boss next week. He refuses. You insist that, surely, some sort of compromise can be found. He's unwilling.

"I'm not leaving without a written response from your unit," he says.

There's nothing for it. Resolve your Confrontation.

MULISH CONTRARIAN   *SKILL* 7   *STAMINA* 6

If you win, turn to **88**. If you lose, turn to **344**.

273

It's already late morning. You crane your neck; it pops like a dislocated shoulder going into joint. You've never briefed an A.D. before. They're just one level below the Deputy Head, the second highest civil servant in your department!

You had planned to finish a longstanding file this morning but, with this A.D. briefing, aren't sure you have enough time.

What will you do?

See if anyone else can help	Turn to **173**
Start your Presentation for the A.D.	Turn to **127**
Do the work you intended to finish	Turn to **65**
Take a breather	Turn to **247**

274

Test your Skill. If you're Successful, turn to **166**. If you're Unsuccessful, turn to **348**.

275

You slump in your chair and stare blankly at the white drop ceiling. You see several black spots; probably black mould from the sixth-floor flood.

"Are you still there?" she says.

Are you? You don't feel like it. You feel quite literally beside yourself, your soul adrift in a nihilistic fog. You need to fight to stay in control. Resolve your internal conflict as a Confrontation.

NASCENT DEPRESSION   *SKILL* 5   *STAMINA* 6

If you win through, turn to **263**. If you completely dissociate, turn to **344**.

276

The drawers and cabinets are dismally bare, though rich in balled up plastic bags. You do find a few things of interest: Napkins, Sugar Packets, and Compostable Plates and Cutlery. You may take any of these with you. There's also a large tin of stale Tim Horton's coffee and a box of Red Rose Tea of dubious vintage. A few stained coffee mugs and a dusty water glass are at the back of a cupboard.

If you wish to rinse out the glass and get some water, turn to **296**. If not, turn to **152**.

277

The D.H. continues. "I'd like to start with a question. What comes to mind when you hear the words, 'Red Tape?' Anyone can answer."

Will you:

Keep your mouth shut	Turn to **267**
Give in to temptation	Turn to **219**

278

You offer Taylor some food. They take half and dig right in. "You're the best," they say over a mouthful. You eat the other half. Restore 2 STAMINA and cross the food off your FRM-0001c.

You turn to leave—turn to **338**.

279

It's now or never for drafting this presentation.

What'll it be?

Now   Turn to **141**
Never   Turn to **370**

280

You're hedged in by grumbling civil servants as the line grinds inexorably over lumpy paving stones. You shuffle toward the Decorative Mantraps, draw level, then finally shuffle through. Lose 1 TIME and 1 STAMINA. Turn to **191**.

281

"Thank you for your patience. An agent will be with you as soon as one is available." The next song in the Hold Hits Top 100 is "More Sax" by Thin Tinny and the Metallic Five. Lose 1 TIME.

Will you hang on (turn to **171**) or go without network access (turn to **223**)?

282

You head back to the office, taking the elevator to the third floor. "Network's back up!" someone shouts. A scattered chorus of cheers rises from the thin Friday crowd. You make for your cubicle. Turn to **83**.

283

Your insides weather the invasion. Restore 1 LUCK and turn to **46**.

284

"That's lateral—I'm holding out for a promotional appointment," she whines. You close your eyes and sigh. Lose 1 STAMINA and turn to **194**.

285

You clear the field of ferocious fowl and mount the steps of the Tower, limping and bleeding but triumphant. The other Civil Servants applaud you. The big executive claps you on the back. You're going to be a Citadel legend. Turn to **393**.

286

"I'm game!" you slur. You're totally fine. Better than ever. Screw your boss and the C.P.D. You know what, you're going to make that your next toast. You shove aside your dishes and take up a fresh glass. "Down with the C.P.D.!" you say, maybe a tad too loudly.

"Down with this wine!" Sammi cheers.

Tully brings you a lava cake dusted with sea salt and pistachios, and two fresh, healthily-sized bourbon old-fashioneds. He raises his own old-fashioned. "Your health!"

You take up your cocktail. Turn to **190**.

287

The milk is silky, cool, and refreshing. Regain 1 STAMINA. You wish André a good day and leave.

"*Bon aventure!*" he says.

Lose 1 TIME and turn to **351**.

288. *"Must be nice to have time for coffee," Barb whines.*

288

The westward windows give you a fine view of several parking lots. The grey labyrinth of cubicles and open Collaboration Areas are eerily quiet. The south side isn't any cheerier. With open, front-to-back cubicles on the right and a long, mushroom-coloured wall on the left, this section feels more like a hallway. You eye the entry to the kitchenette three-quarters down.

"Must be nice to have time for coffee," Barb whines. She's hunched over a monitor in the cubicle beside you, her ancient computer labouring to push air through its dust-clogged fan. She's browsing the jobs.gov website, same as every morning. Her greige cardigan sports a "World's Best Employee" pin she won twenty years ago, but she must have forgotten how. Barb does odd jobs for multiple units now, no one supervisor wanting to be accountable for her performance.

You wish her a good morning.

"Nothing good about it. Weather's terrible," she gripes.

Your reply?

Say it's not all that bad	Turn to **227**
Brush her off and move along	Turn to **308**
Offer to bring her a coffee	Turn to **119**
Tell her about a job elsewhere	Turn to **284**

289

You wing several plates at the geese and pepper the field with cutlery. The huge birds tear at them, attacking with the psychopathic ferocity of a war crime. You charge ahead, hoping the distraction holds.

Turn to **112** but roll one die, not two, when determining how much STAMINA you lose.

290

Your work cell rings. You answer. It's the Associate Deputy's Office (A.D.O.). The A.D. is your boss's boss's boss and head of the entire Branch. A call from them is never good. Never. The Executive Assistant clears her throat. "We received your Report, but the A.D. has questions."

Your stomach drops. Your Report is draft, bold, reaching—it's meant to spark discussion, not for final consideration. The A.D.'s going to have questions. Hard, endless questions. "My Report isn't finalized. I sent it to the Central Policy Directorate (C.P.D.). for comment, not A.D. review."

"I'm sorry, the A.D. has already read it and wants a briefing this afternoon."

"I really d— Did you say briefing?"

"We've scheduled you for late this afternoon. We'll need your materials in advance. I'll send an official tasking to your unit now."

Did you go to your boss's cube this morning? If so, turn to **340**. If not, turn to **232**.

291

Mumbling about running late, you shoulder past the homeless man, who reeks of stale sweat and cigarettes. Turn to **361**.

292

You scrub the stained pot and filter assembly with paper towels. Grabbing a tin of Tim Horton's coffee from under the sink, you brew a pot, filling the area with its revitalizing scent. You fill a chipped mug from the cupboard, sweetened with a wayward sugar packet (at your discretion), and drink the lukewarm liquid. The old beast's element must be giving out. Turn to **299**.

293

You scowl. "What's that supposed to mean?"

"The D.H. wants a central innovation unit, so our A.D. tells me to make one. Only he doesn't give me any staff, just work. Hell."

Your scowl intensifies. "C.P.D. doesn't need a central innovation unit. We have a whole branch for that. My Branch."

"It is what it is," he says. Lose 1 STAMINA.

"It is what it is because people like you keep saying that," you say.

"Okay, whatever. Who are you again?" He turns back to his game. *Click, click, click.*

Your reply?

Remind him who you are	Turn to **322**
March up and demand answers	Turn to **230**

294

"I'm fine, thanks," you say, trying to manifest the lie. Lose 1 STAMINA.

"Glad to hear it. Let's sit," Faye sits at the head of the table.

You sit on her right. Turn to **211**.

295

Have you already encountered Barb (depicted at entry 288)? If so, turn to **269**. If not, turn to **390**.

296

You down one glass of cool water, then another, washing your dry throat. Turn to **299**.

297

You approach the TabarSnak's ancient, purple-and-gold-flecked counter. There's a cash register on top and several worn, plum-coloured stools in front. You don't see André anywhere. "*Je suis* stuck*é, là*!" you hear from behind the counter. Leaning over, you watch André wrestle his torso out of a cabinet's narrow sliding door. He falls back with a muted clatter of flying paper cups. "*Merde, les* frickin' *gobelets*."

He notices you and claws his way up to the register. "Ah, how are you today, *mon ami—ça va—*you're well? What can André get you this morning?"

You chuckle and shake your head. You'd love to engage in a healthy gripe session but don't have the time. Or do you? If you want to chat with André for a bit, turn to **178**. If you'd rather just order, turn to **319**.

298

"What, like this?" you say, showing them your food.

"Hand it over," Taylor says saucily, hand out.

Will you:

Return the food to your bag   Turn to **204**
Split it with them   Turn to **278**

299

Unbeknownst to you, someone laid the Boil Water Advisory Sign face down on the microwave, probably so they could more easily soak their disgusting dishes. The water you ingested is a rich bacterial cocktail that would make a nineteenth-century cholera victim blush. Nothing but a full, sustained boil would sort out that mess.

The first sign of trouble comes with sweating and nausea, followed by violent cramping and other…unpleasantness. You don't recall much after the ambulance arrives but one thing's certain: your workday is at an end. Turn to **344**.

300

You head back to Taylor's cubicle; they're out for the afternoon. You borrow Boggle Groot's supply key and use it to unlock the Supply Closet. Its shelves are a disaster but that's not your objective. You point to two boxes of letter-sized paper on the floor.

"Thanks, man. You're a life saver," Adam says. He grabs a box and hurries back to the copier.

Turns out you are a hero, in a way. Adam is working with Ezra on a major, time sensitive I.B. initiative. This document will make it into a manager's weekend review material (yes, they still insist on hard copies) and seal the whole deal. Gain 1 MERIT for the assist but lose 2 TIME. If you have any time left, turn to **51**.

301

You find six people gathered around a small table. It's an older woman's retirement party. You don't know her but wish her well all the same. You're only six years in; what would it be like to retire after thirty-five? You ask her.

"Oh, you get used to it. Time really gets away from you. But now I get to retire to my cottage and spend more time with my grandkids."

Cottage? Grandkids? It's all you can do to keep up with your student loans and still pay rent, even when the government agrees to pay you. You're years from kids or property ownership. But that's the distant future—your present policy emergency beckons.

You help yourself to some moist, delicious vegan chocolate cupcakes, tortillas, hummus, and tea. Restore 2 STAMINA. Sadly, no napkins. If you have any Napkins, you share out a few out and may take a Vegan Cupcake with you (add it to your FRM-0001c).

You return to your desk. Turn to **395**.

302

You may, if you wish, go for a walk to get some air (turn to **72**). If you'd rather get on with your day, turn to **18**.

303

You sit with colleagues from another unit, chatting about work and your summer plans and projects. You have a grand old time and almost forget what a day it's been. Restore 2 STAMINA for the welcome conversation and a few stolen fries. Time does get away from you, though. Lose 4 TIME. Turn to **282**.

304

You escape the restaurant despite Tully's protestations and pour yourself into an Uber. You're going to have to drink a lot of water to get through this afternoon. Lose 1 SKILL due to persistent loginess. Be glad, for you have escaped a BACHANALEAN RESTERAUN-TEUR with your sobriety relatively intact. Turn to **6**.

305

You chuckle humourlessly and walk on. "Fine, be that way," Taylor says, hurt. It never pays to brush off an office assistant; they wield too much power. Lose 1 LUCK. You head to your cubicle. Turn to **2**.

306

You call up Basma, who is working in the cafeteria. She's more than happy to help. You send her your Presentation. It's returned in short order in much better shape. She needs to head out for the day and won't be available to help again if the opportunity arises. You thank her profusely for her help. Add 1 to your Presentation's version number and turn to **103**.

307

You snatch the brown bag and hurry out of the kitchenette. Add the Stolen Lunch to your FRM-0001c. Lunch theft is a cardinal office sin, however; lose 2 MERIT and your Immortal Soul. Turn to **118**.

308

You shrug and turn away.

"I wish I had time for a coffee. I'm so busy, and my back's acting up again," Barb mewls.

You bite your tongue. Lose 1 STAMINA.

Will you offer to bring her a coffee?

Fine	Turn to **119**
Hell, no	Turn to **194**

309

You tear away, losing a piece of your arm in the process. Lose 1 STAMINA. Gabby, unable to put off the Deputy Head any longer, bustles around the corner. Clutching your wound, you count yourself lucky to only be bleeding. Turn to **40**.

310

Test your Skill adding 1 to the result—you're quite drunk and ravenously hungry. If you're Successful, turn to **304**. If you're Unsuccessful, turn to **218**.

311

Faye holds up her hand. "I need to stop you there. I'm sorry, but this isn't landing the way I'd hoped."

Your heart sinks. You know the key to greater efficiency is leaner upper layers. "If you give me some notes I could go away and work with the C.P.D. Maybe in a few weeks…" You trail off. The A.D. looks confused. "Is something wrong?"

Turn to **400** for your answer.

312

You hand over your ID Badge; cross it off your FRM-0001c (for now). "You'd better be quick," you say roguishly.

"Like the wind," they say in a seductive drawl.

You tell them where you're headed and exchange cell numbers, just in case. Restore 1 STAMIMA for the extra pep in your step. Turn to **332**.

313. Canada geese have taken over the front of the Tower.

313

You head around your building, crossing under the brutalist, concrete arcade beneath the breezeway. The sun breaks through the clouds as you step out into the quad. The half-flooded ring road surrounds the Tower like a moat, but there's a more formidable obstacle: a gaggle of Canada geese have taken over the front lawn, trapping several people at the entrance.

A big man in a blue suit strides forward to shoo the geese away. They respond with a martial flurry and brutal hyønking. They're saying, "This is our territory now. You can all just fuck off." One of them clamps onto the man's jacket and tears it from his hands. Another leaps into the air and chases him to the Tower.

A vagrant is standing on the sidelines. He's shaking his head with a sad smile, like an old solider watching the desperate charge of a forlorn hope. A dog is sitting at his feet, primed and ready. If you know the dog's name, look it up now using **Appendix 1: Electronic Directory Services**.

If not, you still need to get to the Tower; this aggression will not stand.

Will you?

Damn the geese—charge!	Turn to **112**
Use an item from your bag	Turn to **383**

314

You lose your footing, shrieking as you tumble head-long into the jagged pit. *SPLASH!* You mash your head against the bottom of the muddy bowl. Tangled in your bag and jacket, you claw your way to the surface. Sptut-tering gasoline-flavoured water, you beach yourself on the rough asphalt, legs dangling in the watery pit. Your bag slips off into three feet of oily water. Your laptop and cell are surely destroyed. There's no recovering from this; your workday is at an end. Turn to **Appendix 2: Performance Review**.

315

You crash through the weak wall and into a pipe clad in white, fibrous material. The lagging tears, filling the air with hair-like dust particles. You get a good lungful as your head is introduced to the cast-iron pipe beneath.

Hours later, you wake up in hospital, where a grizzled, old doctor gives you your prognosis. It isn't good. Concussion, minor skull fracture, and a lungful of asbestos. The good news is you'll make a full recovery. The bad news is you'll probably die of lung cancer; though, on the plus side, it probably won't hit you for a good thirty or forty years—so you're laughing. At least that's what the doctor says. You suppose he thinks that's funny.

Funny or not, your workday is over. Turn to **344**.

316

You spot some Spare Change on the floor. Grabbing it, you look around, palm out, asking the Universe for a sign not to take it. No sign comes, and no claimant presents themselves, so you accept the cosmic gift. Add Spare Change to your FRM-0001c (or "x2" if you already have some). Turn to **206**.

317

You run full tilt until you're in front of your building. People gawk at the weirdo careening around the corner, but when they hear the furious honking, they understand. You double over, lungs afire, but alive. Turn to **282**.

318

Yes! There's a copy of your Report on your Desktop (note it under "Documents" on your FRM-0001c). You kept it there for just such a situation. Now you can draft a more fulsome Presentation. Turn to **223**.

319

You need snacks, stat!

If you have any Pocket Change, what will you buy?

A coffee and Cinnabonne, of course!	Turn to **15**
Milk and a muffin	Turn to **4**
A cola and bag of chips	Turn to **121**

If you don't have any Pocket Change, or want to save it, you leave, hungry and disappointed. Turn to **351**.

320

You need a break. After packing up your things you decide to hit the washroom. If you want to head to the third-floor washroom and work at your cubicle afterward, turn to **181**. If you'd rather make a quick run to the basement washroom then back to the cafeteria, turn to **214**.

321

It's a slog but you manage, leaving savage comments throughout to pump the brakes on a needlessly rushed report. You email it back and move on with your life. Turn to **3**.

322

You tell him who you are and remind him where you're from.

"Right, right. And you need?" Lose 1 STAMINA and turn to **230**.

323

You return to your cubicle, tired and wanting this day to be over. You have just enough time for a quick break. Will you freshen up in the washroom (turn to **261**), investigate the sound of clapping from across the office (turn to **301**), or eat some Provisions (do so, then turn to **395**)?

324

Test your Skill and add 2 to the result (you're extremely drunk and still somehow hungry). If you're Successful, turn to **304**. If you're Unsuccessful, turn to **286**.

325

The cabinet opens into your kneecap, its bruise fresh from your last encounter with the dial. You grit your teeth to stifle the Litany of Virulent Hate boiling up inside. Lose 1 STAMINA and turn to **213**.

326

You look around furtively, open your bag, and grab a fat Chocolate Bar.

Test your Luck. If you're Lucky, turn to **339**. If you're Unlucky, turn to **157**.

327

"Yeah, sure, just a sec..." you say, rummaging around in your pocket. You bring out a handful of change. It's not much but you hand it over. Cross it off your FRM-0001c and turn to **210**.

328

It's ironic that groups dedicated to the service of others can be so poor at working together. Infighting, harassment, empire-building, Fiscal Battle Royales—the Civil Service has it all. Civil servants constantly forced to struggle against their colleagues have their hearts shriveled and spirits drained until they fade into JADED WRAITHS. These poor souls haunt their units, undermining every project with bitter, defeatist moaning. But this needn't be your fate, not if you cling to hope. Turn to **Appendix 2: Performance Review**.

329

Where is it? No! You left your Folding Umbrella in the office after last week's storm (strike it off your FRM-0001c). Damn it, you're going to get soaked. It's going to be a very uncomfortable morning. Deduct 2 STAMINA and turn to **9**.

330. A backhoe has dug a sizeable, waterlogged crater.

330

You squelch over a grassy median, splash between two long, corrugated metal containers, and stop in your tracks.

"Danger: Construction. Pedestrians Use Main Exit."

The sign hangs on temporary mesh fencing surrounding the parking lot. Inside, a green backhoe sits beside a huge, waterlogged crater. Piles of debris litter the pavement. The entrance is on the far side of the lot—a wide gap blocked by two bright orange sawhorses.

You don't have time for this. You've got to call that Pay Centre Rep before they're swamped by calls. Unfortunately, you don't have data on your work cell or their number in your contacts. To call, you've got to get to your office. There's a way: the fencing in front of you isn't properly mounted; you can certainly slip through.

With the rain pelting down, will you:

Squeeze through the fence	Turn to **70**
Go back and take the long way	Turn to **398**

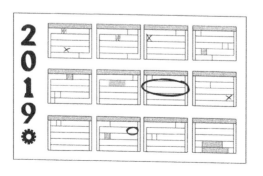

331

You crash headfirst into the wall. It buckles but holds, unlike your grip on consciousness. Turn to **159**.

332

You head out past the TabarSnak. André is switching the hot counter over to lunch.

What route will you take to your office?

The stairs	Turn to **126**
The elevator	Turn to **371**

333

You run for your ever-loving life. Arms pumping, bag flapping, you weave around the slumbering geese, leaping over the final one in a bid for safety. The birds start to their webbed feet and raise a hyønk and cry against you. Wings flail, necks crane, and jaws hiss with malevolence.

Test your Luck. If you're Lucky, turn to **317**. If you're Unlucky, turn to **60**.

334

Sadie clears away your cleanseware. "Now that you're prepared, what's for lunch?" An unsettling way to put it, but okay.

You have three options (all bread is vegan, gluten free; all cheese is cashew; all greens are collard):

Transcendent Tofu Beef Noodles
Bodacious Tempeh Bacon Fried Rice
Mystical Mushroom-Nut Burger

Note down your Transcendent, Bodacious, or Mystical choice and turn to **91**.

335

It's later than you thought! You scramble to bring up the Pay Centre Rep's email but close Outlook in your hurry. You fight to get it back open and bring up the email. Fumbling with your phone, you punch in the number.

Voicemail. *Damn!*

You leave a desperate message and call again ten minutes later. Voicemail. Maybe they're sick, took the day off, or fled the country to get the Albatross Pay System from around their neck. Whatever the cause, this is going to haunt you all day. Lose 1 point each of SKILL, STAMINA, LUCK, and TIME.

Note down that you haven't been paid and turn to **341**.

336

No presentation, huh? Bold, but not necessarily fatal. If you're good. You know the material inside and out. Still, it'll be much harder to convey your ideas in a concise and cohesive manner in the allotted time. The A.D.'s pretty canny. She'll call out any B.S. and pick apart any weak arguments.

Resolve your Presentation as a Confrontation.

BRIEFING FROM THE HIP   *SKILL* 10   *STAMINA* 10

If you win, turn to **255**. If you lose, turn to **311**.

337

What *is* the point? Years are spent on initiatives started by one administration only to be thrown out by the next. As soon as you get something in place management changes and so does your direction. It's endless. Those sapped by the slow turn of the government's screw lose their ability to care, wasting slowly but surely into a DISENCHANTED GHOUL. These sad individuals skulk from doomed project to struggling unit, feeding off misery and frustration. After all, isn't it inevitable? But this needn't be your fate, not if you persist. Turn to **Appendix 2: Performance Review**.

338

"Oh, hey, if I'm not around later, Groot's got the Supply Closet Key." Taylor says, pointing at a *Funko Pop! Holiday Dancing Baby Groot* on their desk. The Supply Closet Key is dangling from Groot's tiny, raised hand. The number "300" is written on it. If you need to get into the Supply Closet later, turn to 300. Note this on your FRM-0001c and restore 1 LUCK for the find.

"Cute, right?" Taylor sets Groot's head dancing and shakes their hips. They take another bite of food. "Okay, bye now!"

You chuckle and make for your cube. Turn to **2**.

339

You get away clean, but not with a clean conscience. Lose 2 MERIT for your shameful thievery. You can eat the Chocolate Bar now or add it to your FRM-0001c for later. Either way, shocking… Turn to **249**.

340

"That's something my boss would han—" No, he's out of the office. Worse, he's been acting for *his* boss, your director, who was seconded to another department a month ago. God, that means you're in charge of this mess.

A chill runs through your body. Lose 1 STAMINA and turn to **172**.

341

Did you clear your email before calling the Pay Centre? If so, turn to **358**. If not, turn to **22**.

342

"Buy me a snack and we're square," you say with a sly grin.

"Deal!" they say, rushing off.

They come back with a Cinnabonne, Muffin or Bag of Chips. Add it to your Provisions but lose 1 TIME. Turn to **312**.

343

It's clear this guy's a DISENCHANTED MANAGER put where he can do the least harm. Sadly, the least harm has already been done. To you. You leave, knowing you aren't going to get anything out of this human sponge.

"Let me know how I can help," he says. *Click, click. Click.*

You cock your head and stand stock-still in the doorway.

Will you:

Walk it off	Turn to **116**
Throw down	Turn to **236**

344

Nuh-uh, no way. That's the last straw. How do they expect you to work under these conditions? Screw it, you're done. Vacation, if not stress leave, awaits.

Your bureaucratic adventure is at an end. One question remains: what annoyed you most?

The totally unreasonable timelines	Turn to **57**
The utter pointlessness of it all	Turn to **337**
The overwhelming resistance	Turn to **328**
Every. Damn. Thing.	Turn to **128**

345. The dreaded Cobra-Chicken.

345

Your feet are utterly soaked, and you're navigating a field of fecal landmines left by geese, but your commute is nearly over. Passing under the big oak tree, you notice (too late!) a Canada goose, terror of every greenspace, on the other side. Its mate and fat, downy young are just behind. My God, you're within spitting distance.

The gander lets out a warning "hyønk" and puts himself between you and the goslings. The Mother Goose answers your surprised cry with a hiss. She rears up with a violent flutter, neck craned like a cobra and toothy beak ready to snap off any appendage that might fall inside. You unsling your bag, a poor weapon against the formidable Canada goose, as it charges.

If you're tired of these parkland bullies having free run of the Citadel and wish to fight, feel free, but subtract 2 SKILL throughout the Confrontation.

COBRA-CHICKEN   *SKILL* 9   *STAMINA* 6

If you (rightly) wish to Escape to your building, turn to **359**. If you fight and win, turn to **266**. If you fight and lose, turn to **58**.

346

You could write a polished presentation in your sleep. In fact, you probably have. You rough out a short, concise, and persuasive PowerPoint presentation. It's draft and going to need updated stats from the C.P.D., but that'll have to wait until the network's back up, hopefully after lunch.

If you have a copy of your Report, note "Presentation v.4" in the Documents box of your FRM-0001c. If you were unable to retrieve a copy of your Report, record "v.3" instead. Saving it to your Desktop, you get up for a quick break. Lose 2 STAMINA and 2 TIME.

If you're in your cubicle, turn to **247**. If you're in the cafeteria, turn to **320**.

347

You show Basma you boss's note. "Huh, I'm not sure who 'J' is, but I heard from a student that the C.P.D.'s director is setting up their own Innovation Affairs group. I think it's called the Office of Innovation Affairs (O.I.A.). They're in a basement or something. Sorry I can't help you more."

She's been very helpful, and you tell her so. Restore 1 LUCK for the intel and note that the O.I.A. sent your report to the A.D.O. Return to **367**.

348

You accidentally kick an errant stone and watch with throat-closing terror as it ricochets into a goose. The feathered monstrosity starts to its feet, hyønking in distress. The gaggle surges like a flash flood, plunging you into a hissing conflagration of flapping fowl. One cracks your knee with its beak as you lurch forward. Lose 1 SKILL and 2 STAMINA. Miraculously, you break through the confused gaggle without further injury. Turn to **317**.

349

You stumble, scraping your palms and shin on the jagged asphalt. Lose 1 SKILL and 1 STAMINA. You haul yourself out of the wet pothole and swing your heavy bag back into position. Limping out of the lot, you hope there are Band-Aids in the kitchenette's First Aid Kit. It's a faint hope.

You make a beeline for your building, passing through several more parking lots and across the big lawn out front. Turn to **345**.

350

It's already late morning. You crane your neck; it pops like a dislocated shoulder going into joint. You've never briefed an A.D. before. They're just one level below the Deputy Head, the second highest civil servant in your department!

You had planned to finish a longstanding file this morning, but now you aren't so sure.

What will you do next?

Start your Presentation for the A.D.   Turn to **127**
Do the work you intended to finish   Turn to **65**
Take a break   Turn to **320**

351

You head out through the cafeteria. Come to think of it, you could work down here over wi-fi. The cafeteria's more spacious than your cramped cubicle and one of the cozy leatherette chairs is free. It'd be a change of scene and you might dodge a few people in the office.

Will you:

Stay here and work   Turn to **364**
Take the stairs to your office   Turn to **258**
Take the elevator to your office   Turn to **30**

352

Your laptop boots up. You type in your network credentials at the login screen, followed by your GOVdocs credentials. You'll need to deal with pay issues, so you bring up MyPay. It takes a while for you to remember which credentials they use. When you do, you're prompted to sign into myKEYFOB. You hunt down those credentials then get into MyPay. Lastly, you log into Outlook, because I.T. is having issues syncing it with your network credentials (a rare issue but you won the lottery).

The Outlook window pops up. Luckily, so do your emails. It haltingly populates with new messages, the scrollbar steadily shrinking as the inbox overflows with today's policy emergencies.

What will you tackle first?

Call the Pay Centre Turn to **64**
Clear your email Turn to **22**

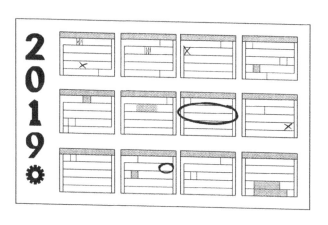

353

"I'll get right on that, Sue," you say, your tone indicating anything but swift action.

She follows you down the hall, heels clacking. "How soon can I get the revised draft?" You inwardly groan. It was a fool's hope, after all. Lose 1 STAMINA.

Will you tell her:

To take it up with your boss	Turn to **90**
Where to stick her draft	Turn to **363**

354

Sammi says goodbye and heads under the brutalist arcade walling in the Tower. You head left along it, passing other workers hunched under dripping umbrellas. Lose 1 TIME and turn to **397**.

355

Oh man, it bit you. That ain't good, because "rabid" wasn't just for colour. You've got rabies. Forget briefing the A.D., you've got a much more important appointment now. One involving a series of extremely painful injections with a mixed chance of survival. Turn to **344**.

356

Hunched and low, you stalk the grey, padded ways of the cube farm in search of sustenance. You come to a crossroads. Which path do you take?

West	Turn to **154**
East	Turn to **269**
South	Turn to **295**

357

Sadie brings out the densest piece of cheesecake you've ever seen. So dense light seems to bend around it. It doesn't look bad, it just doesn't look safe.

No backing out now. She's looking at you expectantly. The pained smile on her face indicates that anything less than praise will result in a shotgun barrel between her teeth.

You dig in. Honestly, the cake is pretty good, but it's a weighty addition to an already monumental meal. You fight to maintain gastric integrity.

Test your Skill. If you're Successful, turn to **283**. If you're Unsuccessful, turn to **115**.

358

An urgent email appears. It's from Grant in the Health and Long-Term Care (H.L.C.) Unit. "Does anyone have the most recent version of the H.L.C. Innovation Cost Analysis? I need to finalize it by C.O.B.!"

Hmm. Lee, P.I.D.'s lead on the file, has been on leave for two months, and you aren't sure to whom your boss assigned it. Still, you're sure you saw it on the Shared Drive the other day. Somewhere.

Will you venture into the labyrinthine folder trees of the Shared Drive? It'd save Grant and advance a key P.I.D. initiative but will take a lot of time and energy. If you feel up to helping, turn to **17**. If you'd rather not, turn to **246**.

359

The Mother Goose bites your calf as you flee (remember to deduct 2 STAMINA for escaping). Turn to **397**.

360

There's no reasoning with a RAVING BUREAUCRAT, not when senior management's involved.

Resolve your Confrontation.

RAVING BUREAUCRAT   *SKILL* 6   *STAMINA* 4

If your Confrontation takes more than 3 *Confrontation Rounds*, lose 1 TIME and turn to **384**. If you defeat her in three rounds or less, turn to **52**. If you lose, turn to **344**.

361

You yank open the side door and hustle out into the rain, rummaging in your bag for your Folding Umbrella.

Test your Luck. If you're Lucky, turn to **8**. If you're Unlucky, turn to **197**.

362

A torrent of empty Band-Aid sleeves spill onto the floor. The First Aid Kit is totally depleted. Your eye twitches. Lose 1 STAMINA. You'll be sure to let some-one know to restock the kit. Unlike certain people. Turn to **152**.

363

There's no getting through to her and you don't have the time. No one likes Sue, and you're about to tell her why.

Resolve your Confrontation.

MICRO-MANAGER   SKILL 7   STAMINA 7

If you win, turn to **34**. If you lose, turn to **344**.

364

The cafeteria is a massive, fluorescently lit hall. Its outer walls are floor to ceiling windows giving you a wonderful view of the front lawn and west parking lots. The floor is a timeless mix of brown tile and grey-blue carpet set with much-abused wood veneer tables and wide metal chairs with brown plastic seats. The entire space has the air of an airport hangar set for a sad Legion banquet. It's pretty deserted.

You head to the front windows and sit in a stretched-out pleather armchair. The chair is comfy, but the drafty air makes your damp clothes feel clammy. Lose 1 STAMINA.

You pull out your battered ThinkPad laptop and throw it open. It powers up with a groan of struggling processors. Your stomach chimes in with a groan of its own, strengthened by the smell of fresh coffee and Cinnabonnes. If you have any Provisions, you may eat some while you work.

Unfortunately, the wi-fi connection is slow today. Lose 1 TIME and turn to **352**.

365. Dominic is running roughshod over Basma.

365

You poke your head into the tiniest of meeting rooms, the lovechild of The Room That Meetings Forgot and The Closet of Misfit Chairs. It's *just* large enough for a round table and three chairs: a blue office chair missing an arm, a black office chair with a back that won't lock, and a brown plastic, metal-framed cafeteria chair.

Basma, your unit's Co-Op Student, is seated at the table. She has a frightened, deer-in-the-headlights-of-a-Mack-truck look. A man is berating her like the Mack truck over said deer. He's got a mop of greying chestnut hair, dark, sunken eyes, and the saggy face of a late-stage Sith Lord. It's Dominic. He's from the old Inter-Governmental Affairs Department.

On paper, your branches work together, but things have been strained since your two departments were merged under I.A.I.G.A.D. The merger meant position cuts with no workload reduction and all the best people jumping ship, those remaining left to fight for resources like parasitic twins in utero.

Will you:

Try to bail out Basma	Turn to **272**
Carry on to the washroom	Turn to **169**

366

What will you do next?

Start your presentation for the A.D.	Turn to **127**
Do the work you had intended to do	Turn to **65**
Take a quick break	Turn to **247**

367

"Thanks for bailing me out. That guy was intense," Basma says. "I thought I could handle his questions, but I didn't expect…that."

You nod sadly. "There are a lot of bad eggs around today for some reason." Why come in on a holiday Friday to harass their colleagues? Do they have nowhere else to be?

Basma smirks. "Must be a planetary alignment or something. Hey, the boss didn't send me any work yesterday. Give me a call this afternoon if you need help."

You thank her. You have a feeling you're going to need all the help you can get. Note down that Basma can help out this afternoon and gain 1 MERIT for bailing her out. Turn to **169**.

368

You're about to get to work when a young man bustles toward you; he's from the other side of the floor— Adam, you think. "Hi, yes! Ezra said you were a wizard with the copier. Can you help? I'm headed next door and need to print a document."

This is a distraction you don't need, but you are handy with the copier. If you want to help Adam, turn to **105**. If you don't have time, turn to **51**.

369

You slip out of sight, your last "Okay then," echoing away as you dash to the washroom. Turn to **199**.

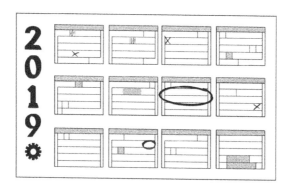

370

You open a web browser and take a deep breath. Before you exhale, a fresh, angry-looking email pops up. "URGENT: For completion and return to D.H.O. by C.O.B. today."

"Fuckssake!" you breathe, spattering the screen with rainbow drops. Always on a Friday. Every time. You scan the email, hoping it doesn't involve your unit or very much work. No, it's for your unit and a hell of a lot of work. It seems the C.P.D. and I.G.A.B drafted an Industry Report and D.H.O. wants I.B.'s comments "through its Innovation lens" before approving this weekend.

Why send it if it's already slated for approval? Why didn't anyone consult the P.I.D. *before* sending it to D.H.O.? Shit. It's going to take a lot of time to skim, let alone comment on.

What will you do?

Grin and bear it	Turn to **62**
Blow it off	Turn to **111**
Phone a friend	Turn to **254**

371

You hop in an empty elevator. The stainless-steel doors slide closed, showing your reflection. You're a wreck. You reach the third floor and make for the washroom. Turn to **199**.

372

Are you determined to brief the A.D. without presentation material? If so, turn to **250**. If you'd rather cancel the briefing, turn to **177**.

373

You scold, cajole, and shame the trolls, driving them behind the yellow smoking line like recalcitrant cattle. They stand there, sullenly unapologetic. They'll slowly creep back, but it'll take a few weeks. Gain 1 MERIT.

You sweep through the front doors, now blessedly smoke-free. Lose 1 TIME and turn to **265**.

You pull open the fridge and look inside. It's filthy. The shelves are packed with reusable containers, brown paper bags, and plastic bags hiding God-knows-what. It's like a WWI battlefield inside, with fresh lunches thrust ahead of old ones like soldiers left in no-man's land. You have the sudden urge to cross yourself, Catholic or not.

You do spot one thing, though: a co-worker's bagged lunch, labelled and sticky-noted, "Hands off!" The guy's a total jerk, but he always has great lunches. Are you desperate enough to Covet Thy Colleague's Lunch, the ultimate office sin?

If you give in to temptation, turn to **307**. If your better angels carry the day, turn to **152**.

375

You hustle through the main exit's turnstiles and out into the rain, rummaging in your bag for your Folding Umbrella.

Test your Luck. If you're Lucky, turn to **98**. If you're Unlucky, turn to **329**.

376

You head toward your cubicle. "O.M.G., you look awful! What happened?" Taylor the Executive Assistant says. They sit three cubicles down from you and are more sardonic than a thrice-divorced philosophy major.

How do you respond?

Murmur something noncommittal	Turn to **305**
Vent about your morning	Turn to **391**
Tell them to mind their own business	Turn to **80**

377

You call up the Pay Centre Rep, praying for an answer.

Test your Luck. If you're Lucky, turn to **133**. If you're Unlucky, turn to **146**.

378. *Your desk is the colour of a late-stage jaundice patient.*

378

Your cubicle is crammed in the south-west corner, its cramped "U" of a desk the colour of a late-stage jaundice patient. On it are two sticky note-festooned monitors, a battered keyboard, and a worn old mouse linked to a docking station. Under it are a narrow stationary cabinet and dial-locking security cabinet wedged perpendicular to one another. You pass through the minimally mandated gap of an entrance, throw your wet bag on the desk, drape your dripping coat over the back of the chair, and plonk onto its stained foam seat.

Scootching your chair into the entrance, you bang your elbow on the keyboard tray and lean over to spin the secure cabinet's lock. This way, that way, the other way, push—*ka-chunk*—you pull open the top drawer.

Test your Skill. If you're Successful, turn to **101**. If you're Unsuccessful, turn to **325**.

379

You show Barb your boss's note and ask if she knows anything about "J." She grimaces. "Your boss's writing is terrible, not that he has an excuse. My carpal tunnel's been acting up all week." You press her on the note.

Test your Skill. If you're Successful, turn to **82**. If you're Unsuccessful, turn to **222**.

380

You cross several parking lots and take a paved path through a thicket full of happily chirping birds. Passing through a gated fence, you enter an older neighbourhood. The houses are quaint, postwar starter homes with peaked roofs, small porches, and clapboard siding. You wander under the old maples and linden trees, happy for the domestic setting if only for a short while.

Too soon, the tranquility is replaced by the whine of saws, clatter of hammers, and din of radio commercials over tinny speakers. The latest transformation has begun. Pits that were houses gape, their neighbours teetering on the precipice of oblivion. Their replacements are three-storey, cookie-cutter McMansions, their mismatched windows and grey exteriors having all the charm of a tax office.

You veer away from the bustle of construction and enjoy the rest of your stroll. Restore 2 STAMINA but lose 3 points of TIME. Turn to **205**.

381

If you didn't talk to the Pay Centre Rep this morning, try to reach them by turning to **377**. If you did, turn to **368**.

382

You check the time. Jesus, it's well into lunch hour! You were out for while. If you didn't already know, the network has gone down again, meaning you can't do much until it's back up. You head to the third floor and the relative peace of your cubicle. Turn to **110**.

383

What, if you have it, will you deploy against these COBRA-CHICKENS?

Napkins	Turn to **135**
Food	Turn to **147**
Compostable Plates and Cutlery	Turn to **289**
None of the above	Turn to **112**

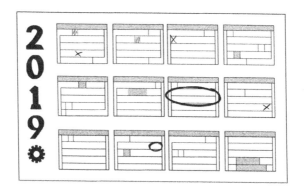

384

Gabby drags you across the office and into the larger boardroom (in that it seats eight, not six). It's standing room only. She blocks the door and joins the others in a brief round of applause. The presentation has already begun.

The D.H. is looking poised and comfortable in a tailored Power Suit. The big TV on the wall keeps flipping between offices across the country. It's a big turnout. You spot yourself on camera and scowl. You need to get out of here.

The D.H. clears their throat. "Thank you all for coming to such an important meeting. I think we can all agree that red tape is a big problem in the Civil Service and that reducing it should be a priority."

You have the sudden urge to point out the irony of a national committee to *reduce* red tape. Do you?

I can't help it!   Turn to **202**
I couldn't say that!   Turn to **158**

385

Ezra hands you a heavy dry-cleaning bag, which you take into a nearby meeting room. Stripping off your wrinkled outfit, you suit up and check your reflection in the privacy glass's glare. The colour is perfect, the fit just right. You look powerful and ready for anything.

Increase your *Initial* SKILL by 1 and restore 2 SKILL; such is the might of the Power Suit (mark it on your FRM-0001c). You fold up your old clothes and leave. Turn to **129**.

386

You call your Office Crush. It goes to voicemail. Where the hell are they? You're going to crush them alright, next time you see them.

You leave a message and slowly pack up your stuff, turning expectantly every time someone arrives. Lose 1 MERIT and 1 TIME.

How will you spend your precious lunch hour?

Get a Temporary Pass	Turn to **89**
If you ran into Sammi, meet them	Turn to **122**
Search the third floor for food	Turn to **356**
Sit in the cafeteria	Turn to **5**
Sit at your desk	Turn to **110**

387

"Yeah, it's what I thought," Drew says. "I put in a change request last night and it's gone through. With luck, you'll get paid in a day or two."

You let out a giddy laugh and nearly cry with relief. You can make rent, buy groceries, AND enjoy your vacation. "Thank you—THANK YOU!" you gush.

"It's nice when this stupid system lets us do anything. I'll send you a confirmation email. It has a link to our survey," they say.

You know what? You'll try to fill it out this time. You slouch in your chair, basking in the warmth that only progress can bring. The Civil Service isn't that bad after all—you've just had a bad run. Restore 1 STAMINA for the boost but lose 1 TIME. Note down that you got paid and turn to **341**.

388

You call up Ezra, who's working in a Starbucks. They're happy to help. You send them your Presentation. It's returned in short order and in much better shape. Unfortunately, Ezra won't be available to help again today if the need arises. You thank them profusely for their help. Add 1 to your Presentation's version number and turn to **103**.

389

Sadie brings you a Collins glass full of bright green slurry flecked with carrot bits. It looks like something that'd be boiling in a Hogwarts cauldron. "What's in it?" you ask.

"That's a trade secret," she says with a disturbing wink.

No going back now. You chug it. It feels like a thick, mealy milkshake that's neither sweet, sour, nor savoury, yet meaty, in a nutty, vegetal kind of way. There's a bit of an ashy aftertaste, but it's not terrible. It's certainly sustaining, and kind of good once you get used to it. Restore 2 STAMINA.

Note down your Potent choice and turn to **334**.

390

Oh no, it's Barb! She's hobbling along the south corridor holding a steaming glass container wrapped in a tea towel. Barb does odd jobs for several units, no one supervisor wanting to be responsible for her performance. You don't have time to get drawn into one of her self-pity parties.

Glancing about like a trapped animal, will you:

Stand your ground	Turn to **174**
Hide in the nearest cubicle	Turn to **260**
Flee the way you came	Turn to **154**

391

You tell Taylor about your misadventures. Lose 1 TIME. They resume typing. "If anyone did that to me, they'd rue the day."

Your reply?

"Can I send them your way, then?"	Turn to **176**
"Big talk from a glorified receptionist."	Turn to **221**
Let your legs do the talking	Turn to **305**

392

You grow hot in every way possible. A blood vessel gives way in your brain. Lose 1 STAMINA. "Listen, lady, my boss is out of the office and this mess is WAY above my pay grade," you growl.

Her manner switches to that of a late-shift 9-1-1 Operator. "Sir, this comes directly from the A.D. Losing your temper won't help matters."

"Help matters? We've got no staff. I'm an Analyst, not a Director. Jesus!"

You're starting to lose it, your tenuous self-control shattering like a pane of glass at an abandoned factory. You need to fight to stay in control.

Resolve your internal conflict as a Confrontation.

IMPENDING MELTDOWN   *SKILL* 9   *STAMINA* 4

If you cool down, turn to **263**. If you break down, turn to **344**.

393

You make your way into the Tower's narrow, green-tiled foyer.

Do you have an ID Badge or Temporary Pass? If not, turn to **11**. If you do, you scan your way through the security gate and take an elevator to the Thirteenth Floor. Your briefing is nigh. Turn to **102**.

394. *"Welcome to hell."*

394

Taking the nearest stairwell, you emerge into a dank corridor that's more steam tunnel than hallway. Large pipes wrapped in dusty white padding (certainly asbestos lagging) line the ceiling. The cinderblock walls are painted chalky Old Hospital Green and the floor is white tile (absolutely asbestos). It feels like you walked into the mid-twentieth century.

Going around a bend and through a set of fire doors, you spot an old, brown sign indicating a left turn to I.A.I.G.A.D. (*wgah-nagl fhtagn*). Another sign that reads, "Medical Waste," points to the right through an archway of overlapping plastic strips. Oh man, the D.O.H. does have labs in this building, and the curiosity is killing you. But you can't. You've got things to do, and your itinerary doesn't include wandering into *The Stand*. You trot the other way with visions of mad experiments and diseased limbs piled in pushcarts. It's for the best; your imagination is far more compelling than anything the Civil Service could conjure.

Leaving behind what could only be a horrible fate, you follow the hall to a blonde wood office door. A piece of printer paper taped to it says, "Manager, Office of Innovation Affairs." Turning the loose handle, you step into a storeroom-*cum*-office. The walls are the same green as the hall outside, and a blonde wood desk has been installed in the back corner.

A man turns in his office chair and looks at you. He's

in his early forties and dressed in khaki pants and a button-down shirt under a blue sweater-vest. "Welcome to hell," he says with a smile, turning back to his computer game of solitaire. *Click, click, click.*

Will you ask:

What he means by that	Turn to **293**
Why he sent your Report to A.D.O.	Turn to **230**

395

It's time to send whatever you've got to A.D.O. Do you have anything to send? If you've drafted your Presentation, turn to **242**. If you haven't drafted anything, turn to **372**.

396

You deke left, then right. The goose slips on the wet turf and goes down! You narrowly evade her clacking maw as you run past. She recovers but too late; you leave the monster behind. Turn to **393**.

397

You fall into the shadow of your squat, six storey office. The Stanley Building. Its concrete is a yellow hue with a mess of light grey patches—mere Band-Aids slapped over structural wounds by indifferent surgeons. Narrow smoked glass windows look down on you like a hundred impatient eyes; a dozen shallow steps span the front like a broad, mocking smile. The forecourt is lined by square planters filled with woody plants that never seem to flower. Still, they're better than the weeds, cigarette butts, and vape cartridges in others. You mount the stairs to the entrance. Turn to **271**.

398

You hurry through the station, the main exit, and back out into the rain. Turn to **9**.

399

"Oh, it's you," Barb mewls.

Your reply?

Ask her about her morning	Turn to **140**
Brush her off and move along	Turn to **132**
Ask if she has any spare snacks	Turn to **155**

Faye nods with realization. "You haven't heard. An election is going to be called. Everything goes on hold in a few weeks."

You shake your head. "But...why ask for this briefing?"

"I liked your grassroots ideas and outside-the-box thinking. I don't see enough of it."

"The government might not change. We could still—"

She chuckles. "Priorities will shift to meet campaign promises. Your ideas are big, the timing just isn't right. Maybe in a year or two. Though, if the other party wins, it could be six or eight. Senior management will likely be shuffled. I might not even be here."

You slouch, physically and emotionally. The Civil Service can't keep flailing away at internal policy this way, lurching back and forth like a bloated hydra that devours itself quadrennially. Can it?

She continues. "I had another reason for bringing you here. Your boss will be moving on soon. He's been acting for your director and trying to run your unit. He needs a change."

It's your turn to chuckle. "Needs a change" is just code for burnout. Or worse. You didn't think it was possible to slump lower, yet here you are.

"I'll be frank: you're a doer, someone who carries on no

matter what's thrown at you. You've kept your team together for months. We can bump you up to Acting Senior Analyst until we find you a new Director. Might as well get paid for the work you're already doing."

More responsibility? You can hardly deal with what's already on your plate. You hope your boss completed the paperwork for those co-op students. There's so much work. You can't do it all *and* manage the unit. Besides, it'll take months to backfill your position and longer for your replacement to get up to speed.

"I can see that this is a lot. Go home. Take your vacation to think it over. Come back refreshed and ready to tackle a whole new set of problems."

You nod and thank her, though for what you don't know. Shouldering your bag, you make for the door, wondering how you're going to get through the rest of the month.

I don't know. It's all pensionable. Only 7,120 working days until retirement. More or less. At the very least you've got two weeks to yourself, hopefully with pay, and can put off thinking about this mess for a few more days. Honestly, you just want to get home.

Who knows, maybe 2020 will be easier.

Turn to **Appendix 2: Performance Review**.

Appendix 1: Electronic Directory Services (E.D.S.)

Welcome to E.D.S.

The E.D.S. provides a directory of civil servants. Information in this directory is supplied and updated by individual departments and may be woefully out of date. Also, some units don't use E.D.S. or list all their employees. Good luck.

Search in : National Headquarters

Instructions : Convert each letter in the name/acronym to a number, sum the total and turn to that entry.

Example 1 : "OIGA" = O+I+G+A = 15+9+7+1 = 32

A	1	J	10	S	19
B	2	K	11	T	20
C	3	L	12	U	21
D	4	M	13	V	22
E	5	N	14	W	23
F	6	O	15	X	24
G	7	P	16	Y	25
H	8	Q	17	Z	26
I	9	R	18		

Appendix 2: Performance Review

Thank you for completing *The Citadel of Bureaucracy*, the Civil Service equivalent of the Kobayashi Maru.

To assess your performance, adjust your total MERIT using the following modifiers:

No cheating	+1
Rolled dice	+1
Failed to reach the Pay Centre Rep	-1
Didn't draft a Presentation for the A.D.	-1
Called forth *Ye Liveliest Awfulness*	-1

If you're a MAD COMPLETIONIST, know that there are 9 potential MERIT points (21 posthumous), including the two bonuses above.

Total Merit	Performance Rating
Didn't reach the office	Unable to Assess
≤ 0	Did Not Meet
1-2	Needs Improvement
3-6	Succeeded
7-8	Exceeded
9+	Surpassed

Unable to Assess

Ouch, you didn't even make it to the office. Hard luck. As with a small number of other civil servants, there simply isn't enough data to assess your performance. Like a drunk trying to light the wrong end of a cigarette, I recommend you give it another try.

Zero or Below: Did Not Meet

You're in the bottom fraction of a percent (that's right, a percent of a percent) of civil servants. That's an achievement of its own in the disciplinary-averse Civil Service. Unless you've got a horribly vindictive manager. The only way to improve in this scenario is another playthrough, and *maybe* do a few things differently.

1-2: Needs Improvement

Welcome to the bottom percent. You've got spunk, kid, but just aren't there yet. Either you aren't producing or have some interpersonal issues to work on. Either way, your Action Plan includes another playthrough. Just be sure to apply all Lessons Learned.

3-6: Succeeded

Like an overwhelming majority of civil servants, you met all expectations regardless of effort. It's fine. You might feel that your performance warrants a higher rating, but, really, you should just check that box in your Performance Agreement. After all, doing so only indicates that the process has taken place, not agreement with the rating. Besides, challenging a "Succeeded" rating will be, at best, a Pyrrhic victory. If not a Greek tragedy.

7-8: Exceeded

Well done. I guess you really are in one of the highest performing civil services in the world. That should be heartening but it's not. Not after what you went through. Don't let that get you down, you owned this scenario, exceeding expectations and generating strong results well above those required for your position. If you aren't already in civil service, you should consider joining. We need more people like you.

9+: Surpassed

You're in the top percentile. You gave it your all and then some, advancing not only the I.B.'s Strategic and Organizational Objectives, but also the Civil Service's Vision, Mission, and Guiding Principles. More importantly, you managed to make an exceptional contribution to the people you serve and the lives of your colleagues. Sure, it was hugely draining, and you're helping to prop up an ailing organization, but it's only a matter of time until you swell the ranks of the Executive Cadre. Unless you're dead. Either way, you have my sympathies.

Acknowledgements

A big thank you to my playtesters, Stephanie Lennon, Janae Schiele, Rémi Savard, and Andrew Smith. As always, I couldn't have written this without the tireless support of my wife and best friend, Jen Kershaw.

J.D. Mitchell has spent his life and career subject to the inflexible caprices of bureaucracies public, private, municipal, federal, secular, and religious. Late one morning, after synthesizing several dissociated policies and process maps, he let out a shuddering cry of atavistic dread. Racing from his cubicle, he fled to a shack in the wilds of Ontario, never to return. He's still there, churning out dark and irreverent fiction to soothe his dark and irreverent soul.

Matt Herring is a graduate of Sheridan College's Classical Animation Program. He has worked as a professional animator for over twenty years, on series such as *My Little Pony: Friendship is Magic* (as Art Director for two years), *Carmen Sandiego*, and *Chilly Beach*.

Mason T. O'Halloran holds a Bachelor of Fine Arts in Illustration from the San Francisco Academy of Art. He is the author and illustrator of *The Catonaut* graphic novels and the children's book, *The Kittenauts Explore the Solar System*.

Please consider leaving a review online or sharing your thoughts via social media.

Thanks for your kind support!

Sign up for my quarterly newsletter at
www.jdmitchellwriter.com
for author updates and giveaways.

Made in the USA
Las Vegas, NV
10 December 2024